"This lady put herself so often in my way."

The History and
Remarkable Life
of the truly
Honourable Colonel Jacque

Volume II

———

# Daniel Defoe

———

Edited by GEORGE A. AITKIN

with

Illustrations by J. B. YEATS

———

LONDON:

J. M. DENT AND COMPANY

1902

## LIST OF ILLUSTRATIONS

# THE LIFE OF

# COLONEL JACQUE

IT was three years after this before I could get
things in order, fit for my leaving the country.
In this time I delivered my tutor from his bondage,
and would have given him his liberty, but, to my great
disappointment, I found that I could not empower
him to go for England till his time was expired, according to the certificate of his transportation, which
was registered; so I made him one of my overseers,
and thereby raised him gradually to a prospect of
living in the same manner and by the like steps that
my good benefactor raised me, only that I did not
assist him to enter upon planting for himself as I was
assisted, neither was I upon the spot to do it. But this
man's diligence and honest application, even unassisted,
delivered himself, [though not] any farther than, as I
say, by making him an overseer, which was only a
present ease and deliverance to him from the hard
labour and fare which he endured as a servant.

However, in this trust he behaved so faithfully and
so diligently that it recommended him in the country;
and when I came back I found him in circumstances

II.

A

very different from what I left him in, besides his being my principal manager for near twenty years, as you shall hear in its place.

I mention these things the more at large that, if any unhappy wretch who may have the disaster to fall into such circumstances as these may come to see this account, they may learn the following short lessons from these examples :—

I. That Virginia and a state of transportation may be the happiest place and condition they were ever in for this life, as, by a sincere repentance and a diligent application to the business they are put to, they are effectually delivered from a life of flagrant wickedness and put in a perfect new condition, in which they have no temptation to the crimes they formerly committed, and have a prospect of advantage for the future.

II. That in Virginia the meanest and most despicable creature, after his time of servitude is expired, if he will but apply himself with diligence and industry to the business of the country, is sure (life and health supposed) both of living well and growing rich.

As this is a foundation which the most unfortunate wretch alive is entitled to, a transported felon is, in my opinion, a much happier man than the most prosperous untaken thief in the nation. Nor are those poor young people so much in the wrong as some imagine them to be that go voluntarily over to those countries, and in order to get themselves carried over and placed there, freely bind themselves there, especially if the persons into whose hands they fall do anything honestly by them ; for, as it is to be supposed that those poor people knew not what course to take before, or had miscarried in their conduct before, here they are sure to be immediately provided for, and, after the expiration of their time, to be put in a condition to provide for themselves. But I return to my own story, which now begins a new scene.

I was now making provision for my going to England. After having settled my plantation in such hands as was fully to my satisfaction, my first work was to furnish myself with such a stock of goods and money as might be sufficient for my occasions abroad, and particularly might allow me to make large returns to Maryland, for the use and supply of all my plantations. But when I came to look nearer into the voyage, it occurred to me that it would not be prudent to put my cargo all on board the same ship that I went in; so I shipped at several times five hundred hogsheads of tobacco in several ships for England, giving notice to my correspondent in London that I would embark about such a time to come over myself, and ordering him to insure for a considerable sum, proportioned to the value of my cargo.

About two months after this I left the place, and embarked for England in a stout ship, carrying twenty-four guns and about six hundred hogsheads of tobacco, and we left the capes of Virginia on the 1st of August. We had a very sour and rough voyage for the first fortnight, though it was in a season so generally noted for good weather.

After we had been about eleven days at sea, having the wind most part of the time blowing very hard at west, or between the west and north-west, by which we were carried a great way farther to the eastward than they usually go in their course for England, we met with a furious tempest, which held us five days, blowing most of the time excessive hard, and by which we were obliged to run away afore the wind, as the seamen call it, wheresoever it was our lot to go. By this storm our ship was greatly damaged, and some leaks we had, but not so bad that by the diligence of the seamen they were stopped. However, the captain, after having beaten up again as well as he could against the weather, and the sea going very high, at length he resolved to go away for the Bermudas.

I was not seaman enough to understand what the reason of their disputes was, but in their running for the islands it seems they overshot the latitude, and could never reach the islands of Bermudas again. The master and the mate differed to an extremity about this, their reckonings being more than usually wide of one another, the storm having driven them a little out of their knowledge. The master, being a positive man, insulted the mate about it, and threatened to expose him for it when he came to England. The mate was an excellent sea artist and an experienced sailor, but withal a modest man, and though he insisted upon his being right, did it in respectful terms and as it became him. But after several days' dispute, when the weather came to abate and the heavens to clear up, that they could take their observations and know where they were, it appeared that the mate's account was right, and the captain was mistaken; for they were then in the latitude of 29 degrees, and quite out of the wake of the Bermudas.

The mate made no indecent use of the discovery at all, and the captain, being convinced, carried it civilly to him, and so the heats were over among them; but the next question was, what they should do next. Some were for going one way, some another; but all agreed that they were not in a condition to go on the direct course for England, unless they could have a southerly or south-west wind, which had not been our fate since we came to sea.

Upon the whole, they resolved by consent to steer away to the Canaries, which was the nearest land they could make except the Cape de Verde Islands, which were too much to the southward for us, if it could be avoided.

Upon this they stood away N.E., and the wind hanging still westerly, or to the northward of the west, we made good way, and in about fifteen days' sail we made the Pico Teneriffe, being a monstrous hill in one of the Canary Islands. Here we refreshed ourselves, got fresh water and some fresh provisions, and plenty of excellent wine, but no harbour to run into, to take care of the ship, which was leaky and tender, having had so much very bad weather; so we were obliged to do as well as we could, and put to sea again, after riding at the Canaries four days only.

From the Canaries we had tolerable weather and a smooth sea till we came into the soundings—so they call the mouth of the British Channel—and the wind blowing hard at the N. and the N.W. obliged us to keep a larger offing, as the seamen call it, at our entrance into the Channel; when, behold! in the grey of the morning a French cruiser or privateer of twenty-six guns appeared, and crowded after us with all the sail they could make. In short, our captain exchanged a broadside or two with them, which was terrible work to me, for I had never seen such before, the French-man's guns having raked us, and killed and wounded six of our best men.

In short, after a fight long enough to show us that if we would not be taken we must resolve to sink by her side, for there was no room to expect deliverance, and a fight long enough to save the master's credit, we were taken, and the ship carried away to St Malo.

I was not much concerned for the loss I had in the ship, because I knew I had sufficient in the world somewhere or other; but as I was effectually stripped of everything I had about me, and even almost my clothes from my back, I was in but a very indifferent

condition. But somebody informing the captain of the
privateer, that I was a passenger and a merchant, he
called for me and inquired into my circumstances, and
coming to hear from myself how I had been used,
obliged the seamen to give me a coat and hat and a
pair of shoes, which they had taken off me, and himself gave me a morning gown of his own to wear
while I was in his ship, and, to give him his due,
treated me very well.

I had, however, besides my being taken, the mortification to be detained on board the cruiser, and
seeing the ship I was in manned with Frenchmen and
sent away, as above, for St Malo ; and this was a
greater mortification to me afterwards, when, being
brought into St Malo, I heard that our own ship was
retaken in her passage to St Malo by an English
man-of-war and carried to Portsmouth.

When our ship was sent away the *Rover* cruised
abroad again in the mouth of the Channel for some
time, but met with no purchase. At last they made a
sail, which proved to be one of their nation and one
of their own trade, from whom they learned, the news
having been carried to England that some French
privateers lay off and on in the soundings, that three
English men-of-war were come out from Plymouth
on purpose to cruise in the Channel, and that they
would certainly meet with us. Upon this intelligence
the Frenchman, a bold, brave fellow, far from shrink-
ing from his work, stands away N.E. for St George's
Channel, and in the latitude of 48 degrees and a half,
unhappily enough, meets with a large and rich English
ship, bound home from Jamaica. It was in the grey
of the morning, and very clear, when a man on the
roundtop cried out, "*Au voile*, a sail." I was in hopes
indeed it had been the English men-of-war, and by
the hurry and clutter they were in to get all ready

for a fight, I concluded it was so, and got out of my
hammock (for I had no cabin to lie in) that I might
see what it was; but I soon found that my hopes
were in vain, and it was on the wrong side; for that
that being on our larboard bow, the ship lying then
northward to make the coast of Ireland, by the time I
was turned out I could perceive they had all their
sails bent and full, having begun to chase, and making
great way. On the other hand, it was evident the
ship saw them too, and knew what they were, and, to
avoid them, stretched away with all the canvas they
could lay on for the coast of Ireland, to run in there
for harbour.

Our privateer, it was plain, infinitely outsailed her,
running two foot for her one, and towards evening
came up with them. Had they been able to have
held it but six hours longer they would have got into
Limerick River, or somewhere under shore, so that we
should not have ventured upon them. But we came up
with them, and the captain, when he saw there was
no remedy, bravely brought to and prepared to fight.
She was a ship of thirty guns, but deep in the sea,
cumbered between decks with goods, and could not
run out her lower-deck guns, the sea also going pretty
high, though at last she ventured to open her gun-
room ports and fire with three guns on a side. But
her worst fate was, she sailed heavy, being deep loaden,
and the Frenchman had run up by her side and
poured in his broadside, and was soon ready again.
However, as she was well manned too, and that the
English sailors bestirred themselves, they gave us
their broadsides too very nimbly and heartily, and I
found the Frenchman had a great many men killed at
the first brush. But the next was worse, for the English
ship, though she did not sail so well as the Frenchman,
was a bigger ship and strong built, and as we (the

French) bore down upon them again, the English run
boldly on board us, and laid thwart our hawse, lashing
themselves fast to us. Then it was that the English
captain run out his lower tier of guns, and indeed tore
the Frenchman so, that, had he held it, the privateer
would have had the worst of it. But the Frenchman, with admirable readiness, indeed, and courage,
the captain appearing everywhere with his sword in
his hand, bestirred themselves, and loosing themselves
from the English ship, thrusting her off with brooms,
and pouring their small shot so thick that the other
could not appear upon deck; I say, clearing themselves thus, they came to lie a-broadside of each other,
when, by long firing, the English ship was at length
disabled, her mizzen-mast and bowsprit shot away, and,
which was worst of all, her captain killed; so that,
after a fight which held all night—for they fought in
the dark—and part of the next day, they were obliged
to strike.

I was civilly desired by the French captain to go
down into the hold while the fight held, and, besides
the civility of it, I found he was not willing I should
be upon deck. Perhaps he thought I might have some
opportunity to do hurt, though I know not how it could
be. However, I was very ready to go down, for I had
no mind to be killed, especially by my own friends;
so I went down and sat by the surgeon, and had the
opportunity to find that, the first broadside the English
fired, seven wounded men were brought down to the
surgeon, and three-and-thirty more afterwards, that is to
say, when the English lay thwart their bow; and after
they cleared themselves there were about eleven more;
so that they had one-and-fifty men wounded and about
two-and-twenty killed. The Englishman had eighteen
men killed and wounded, among whom was the captain.

The French captain, however, triumphed in his prize;

for it was an exceeding rich ship, having abundance of silver on board. And after the ship was taken and they had plundered all the great cabin afforded, which was very considerable, the mate promised the captain that, if he would give him his liberty, he would discover six thousand pieces of eight to him privately, which none of the men should know of. The captain engaged, and gave it under his hand to set him at liberty as soon as he came on shore. Accordingly, in the night, after all was either turned in, as they call it, or employed on the duty of the watch, the captain and the mate of the prize went on board, and having faithfully discovered the money, which lay in a place made on purpose to conceal it, the captain resolved to let it lie till they arrived, and then he conveyed it on shore for his own use ; so that the owners, nor the seamen, ever came to any share of it, which, by the way, was a fraud in the captain. But the mate paid his ransom by the discovery, and the captain gave him his liberty very punctually, as he had promised, and two hundred pieces of eight to carry him to England and to make good his losses.

When he had made this prize, the captain thought of nothing more than how to get safe to France with her, for she was a ship sufficient to enrich all his men and his owners also. The account of her cargo, by the captain's books, of which I took a copy, was in general :

       260 hogsheads of sugar.
       187 smaller casks of sugar.
       176 barrels of indigo.
        28 casks of pimento.
        42 bags of cotton wool.
        80 cwt. of elephants' teeth.
        60 small casks of rum.
   18,000 pieces of eight, besides the six thou-
         sand concealed.

Several parcels of drugs, tortoise-shell, sweetmeats, called succades, chocolate, lime juice, and other things of considerable value.

This was a terrible loss among the English merchants, and a noble booty for the rogues that took it ; but as it was in open war and by fair fighting, as they call it, there was no objection to be made against them, and, to give them their due, they fought bravely for it.

The captain was not so bold as to meeting the English men-of-war before, but he was as wary now ; for, having a prize of such value in his hands, he was resolved not to lose her again, if he could help it. So he stood away to the southward, and that so far that I once thought he was resolved to go into the Straits, and home by Marseilles. But having sailed to the latitude of 45 degrees 3 quarters, or thereabouts, he steered away east, into the bottom of the Bay of Biscay, and carried us all into the river of Bordeaux, where, on notice of his arrival with such a prize, his owners or principals came overland to see him, and where they consulted what to do with her. The money they secured, to be sure, and some of the cargo ; but the ships sailed afterwards along the coast to St Malo, taking the opportunity of some French men-of-war which were cruising on the coast to be their convoy as far as Ushant.

Here the captain rewarded and dismissed the English mate, as I have said, who got a passage from thence to Dieppe by sea, and after that into England, by the help of a passport, through Flanders to Ostend. The captain, it seems, the more willingly shipped him off that he might not discover to others what he had discovered to him.

I was now at Bordeaux, in France, and the captain asked me one morning what I intended to do. I did

not understand him at first, but he soon gave me to understand that I was now either to be delivered up to the state as an English prisoner, and so be carried to Dinan, in Brittany, or to find means to have myself exchanged, or to pay my ransom, and this ransom he told me at first was three hundred crowns.

I knew not what to do, but desired he would give me time to write to England to my friends ; for that I had a cargo of goods sent to them by me from Virginia, but I did not know but it might have fallen into such hands as his were, and if it was, I knew not what would be my fate. He readily granted that; so I wrote by the post, and had the satisfaction, in answer to it, to hear that the ship I was taken in had been retaken, and carried into Portsmouth ; which I doubted would have made my new master more strict, and perhaps insolent ; but he said nothing of it to me, nor I to him, though, as I afterwards understood, he had advice of it before.

However, this was a help to me, and served to more than pay my ransom to the captain. And my correspondent in London, hearing of my being alive and at Bordeaux, immediately sent me a letter of credit upon an English merchant at Bordeaux for whatever I might have occasion for. As soon as I received this I went to the merchant, who honoured the letter of credit, and told me I should have what money I pleased. But as I, who was before a mere stranger in the place and knew not what course to take, had now, as it were, a friend to communicate my affairs to and consult with, as soon as I told him my case, "Hold," says he ; "if that be your case, I may perhaps find a way to get you off without a ransom."

There was, it seems, a ship bound home to France from Martinico, taken off Cape Finisterre by an English man-of-war, and a merchant of Rochelle,

being a passenger, was taken on board, and brought
into Plymouth. This man had made great solicitation
by his friends to be exchanged, pleading poverty, and
that he was unable to pay any ransom. My friend told
me something of it, but not much, only bade me not be
too forward to pay any money to the captain, but pretend I could not hear from England. This I did till
the captain appeared impatient.

After some time the captain told me I had used him
ill; that I had made him expect a ransom, and he had
treated me courteously and been at expense to subsist
me, and that I held him in suspense, but that, in short,
if I did not procure the money, he would send me to
Dinan in ten days, to lie there as the king's prisoner
till I should be exchanged. My merchant gave me my
cue, and by his direction I answered I was very sensible of his civility, and sorry he should lose what
expenses he had been at, but that I found my friends
forgot me, and what to do I did not know, and that,
rather than impose upon him, I must submit to go to
Dinan, or where he thought fit to send me; but that if
ever I obtained my liberty, and came into England, I
would not fail to reimburse him what expense he had
been at for my subsistence; and so, in short, made my
case very bad in all my discourse. He shook his head
and said little, but the next day entered me in the
list of English prisoners to be at the king's charge, as
appointed by the intendant of the place, and to be sent
away into Brittany.

I was then out of the captain's power, and immediately the merchant, with two others who were friends
to the merchant prisoner at Plymouth, went to the intendant and gained an order for the exchange, and my
friend giving security for my being forthcoming, in case
the other was not delivered, I had my liberty immediately, and went home with him to his house.

Thus we bilked the captain of his ransom money. But, however, my friend went to him, and letting him know that I was exchanged by the governor's order, paid him whatever he could say he was in disburse on my account; and it was not then in the captain's power to object, or to claim anything for a ransom.

I got passage from hence to Dunkirk on board a French vessel, and having a certificate of an exchanged prisoner from the intendant at Bordeaux, I had a passport given me to go into the Spanish Netherlands, and so whither I pleased.

Accordingly I came to Ghent, in April ——, just as the armies were going to take the field. I had no dislike to the business of the army, but I thought I was a little above it now, and had other things to look to; for that, in my opinion, nobody went into the field but those that could not live at home. And yet I resolved to see the manner of it a little too, so, having made an acquaintance with an English officer quartered at Ghent, I told him my intention, and he invited me to go with him, and offered me his protection as a volunteer, that I should quarter with him in his tent, and live as I would, and either carry arms or not, as I saw occasion.

The campaign was none of the hardest that had been, or was like to be; so that I had the diversion of seeing the service, as it was proper to call it, without much hazard. Indeed I did not see any considerable action, for there was not much fighting that campaign. As to the merit of the cause on either side, I knew nothing of it, nor had I suffered any of the disputes about it to enter into my thoughts. The Prince of Orange had been made king of England, and the English troops were all on his side; and I heard a great deal of swearing and damning for King William among the soldiers. But as for fighting, I observed the French

beat them several times, and particularly the regiment my friend belonged to was surrounded in a village where they were posted, I knew not upon what occasion, and all taken prisoners. But by great good hap, I, being not in service, and so not in command, was strolled away that day to see the country about ; for it was my delight to see the strong towns, and observe the beauty of their fortifications ; and while I diverted myself thus, I had the happy deliverance of not being taken by the French for that time.

When I came back I found the enemy possessed of the town, but as I was no soldier they did me no harm, and having my French passport in my pocket, they gave me leave to go to Nieuport, where I took the packet-boat and came over to England, landing at Deal instead of Dover, the weather forcing us into the Downs ; and thus my short campaign ended, and this was my second essay at the trade of soldiering.

When I came to London I was very well received by my friend, to whom I had consigned my effects, and I found myself in very good circumstances ; for all my goods, which, as above, by several ships, I had consigned to him, came safe to hand ; and my overseers that I had left behind had shipped at several times four hundred hogsheads of tobacco to my correspondent in my absence, being the product of my plantation, or part of it, for the time of my being abroad ; so that I had above £1000 in my factor's hands, two hundred hogsheads of tobacco besides left in hand, not sold.

I had nothing to do now but entirely to conceal myself from all that had any knowledge of me before. And this was the easiest thing in the world to do ; for I was grown out of everybody's knowledge, and most of those I had known were grown out of mine. My captain, who went with me, or, rather, who carried me away, I found, by inquiring at the proper place, had

been rambling about the world, came to London, fell
into his own trade, which he could not forbear, and
growing an eminent highwayman, had made his exit
at the gallows, after a life of fourteen years' most
exquisite and successful rogueries, the particulars of
which would make, as I observed, an admirable history. My other brother Jacque, who I called major,
followed the like wicked trade, but was a man of more
gallantry and generosity; and having committed innumerable depredations upon mankind, yet had always
so much dexterity as to bring himself off, till at length
he was laid fast in Newgate, and loaded with irons,
and would certainly have gone the same way as the
captain, but he was so dexterous a rogue that no gaol,
no fetters, would hold him; and he, with two more,
found means to knock off their irons, worked their way
through the wall of the prison, and let themselves down
on the outside in the night. So escaping, they found
means to get into France, where he followed the same
trade, and with so much success that he grew famous
by the name of Anthony, and had the honour, with
three of his comrades, whom he had taught the English
way of robbing generously, as they called it, without
murdering or wounding, or ill-using those they robbed;
—I say, he had the honour to be broke upon the wheel
at the Greve in Paris.

All these things I found means to be fully informed
of, and to have a long account of the particulars of their
conduct from some of their comrades who had the
good fortune to escape, and who I got the knowledge
of without letting them so much as guess at who I was
or upon what account I inquired.

I was now at the height of my good fortune.
Indeed I was in very good circumstances, and being
of a frugal temper from the beginning, I saved things
together as they came, and yet lived very well too.

Particularly I had the reputation of a very considerable merchant, and one that came over vastly rich from Virginia; and as I frequently bought supplies for my several families and plantations there as they wrote to me for them, so I passed, I say, for a great merchant.

I lived single, indeed, and in lodgings, but I began to be very well known, and though I had subscribed my name only "Jack" to my particular correspondent, yet the French, among whom I lived near a year, as I have said, not understanding what Jack meant, called me Monsieur Jacques and Colonel Jacques, and so gradually Colonel Jacque. So I was called in the certificate of exchanging me with the other prisoner, so that I went so also into Flanders; upon which, and seeing my certificate of exchange, as above, I was called Colonel Jacques in England by my friend who I called correspondent. And thus I passed for a foreigner and a Frenchman, and I was infinitely fond of having everybody take me for a Frenchman; and as I spoke French very well, having learned it by continuing so long among them, so I went constantly to the French church in London, and spoke French upon all occasions as much as I could; and, to complete the appearance of it, I got me a French servant to do my business—I mean as to my merchandise, which only consisted in receiving and disposing of tobacco, of which I had about five hundred to six hundred hogsheads a year from my own plantations, and in supplying my people with necessaries as they wanted them.

In this private condition I continued about two years more, when the devil, owing me a spleen ever since I refused being a thief, paid me home, with my interest, by laying a snare in my way which had almost ruined me.

There dwelt a lady in the house opposite to the

house I lodged in, who made an extraordinary figure indeed. She went very well dressed, and was a most beautiful person. She was well-bred, sung admirably fine, and sometimes I could hear her very distinctly, the houses being over against one another, in a narrow court, not much unlike Three King Court in Lombard Street.

This lady put herself so often in my way that I could not in good manners forbear taking notice of her, and giving her the ceremony of my hat when I saw her at her window, or at the door, or when I passed her in the court; so that we became almost acquainted at a distance. Sometimes she also visited at the house I lodged at, and it was generally contrived that I should be introduced when she came, and thus by degrees we became more intimately acquainted, and often conversed together in the family, but always in public, at least for a great while.

I was a mere boy in the affair of love, and knew the least of what belonged to a woman of any man in Europe of my age. The thoughts of a wife, much less of a mistress, had never so much as taken the least hold of my head, and I had been till now as perfectly un-acquainted with the sex, and as unconcerned about them, as I was when I was ten years old, and lay in a heap of ashes at the glass-house.

But I know not by what witchcraft in the conver-sation of this woman, and her singling me out upon several occasions, I began to be ensnared, I knew not how, or to what end; and was on a sudden so em-barrassed in my thoughts about her that, like a charm, she had me always in her circle. If she had not been one of the subtlest women on earth, she could never have brought me to have given myself the least trouble about her, but I was drawn in by the magic of a genius capable to deceive a more wary capacity than mine, and it was impossible to resist her.

She attacked me without ceasing, with the fineness of her conduct, and with arts which were impossible to be ineffectual. She was ever, as it were, in my view, often in my company, and yet kept herself so on the reserve, so surrounded continually with obstructions, that for several months after she could perceive I sought an opportunity to speak to her, she rendered it impossible; nor could I ever break in upon her, she kept her guard so well.

This rigid behaviour was the greatest mystery that could be, considering, at the same time, that she never declined my seeing her or conversing with me in public. But she held it on; she took care never to sit next me, that I might slip no paper into her hand or speak softly to her; she kept somebody or other always between, that I could never come up to her; and thus, as if she was resolved really to have nothing to do with me, she held me at the bay several months.

All this while nothing was more certain than that she intended to have me, if she could catch; and it was indeed a kind of a catch, for she managed all by art, and drew me in with the most resolute backwardness, that it was almost impossible not to be deceived by it. On the other hand, she did not appear to be a woman despicable, neither was she poor, or in a condition that should require so much art to draw any man in; but the cheat was really on my side; for she was unhappily told that I was vastly rich, a great merchant, and that she would live like a queen; which I was not at all instrumental in putting upon her, neither did I know that she went upon that motive.

She was too cunning to let me perceive how easy she was to be had; on the contrary, she run all the hazards of bringing me to neglect her entirely that one would think any woman in the world could do. And I have wondered often since how that it was possible it should fail of making me perfectly averse to her; for as I had a perfect indifference for the whole sex, and never till then entertained any notion of them, they were no more to me than a picture hanging up against a wall.

As we conversed freely together in public, so she took a great many occasions to rally the men, and the weakness they were guilty of in letting the women insult them as they did. She thought if the men had not been fools, marriage had been only treaties of peace between two neighbours, or alliances offensive or defensive, which must necessarily have been carried on sometimes by interviews and personal treaties, but oftener by ambassadors, agents, and emissaries on both sides; but that the women had outwitted us, and brought us upon our knees, and made us whine after them, and lower ourselves, so as we could never pretend to gain our equality again.

I told her I thought it was a decency to the ladies to give them the advantage of denying a little, that they might be courted, and that I should not like a woman the worse for denying me. "I expect it, madam," says I, "when I wait on you to-morrow;" intimating that I intended it. "You shan't be deceived, sir," says she, "for I'll deny now, before you ask me the question."

I was dashed so effectually with so malicious, so devilish an answer that I returned with a little sullenness, "I shan't trespass upon you yet, madam; and I shall be very careful not to offend you when I do."

"It is the greatest token of your respect, sir," says she, "that you are able to bestow upon me, and the most agreeable too, except one, which I will not be out of hopes of obtaining of you in a little time."

"What is in my power to oblige you in, madam," said I, "you may command me in at any time, especially the way we are talking of." This I spoke still with a resentment very sincere.

"It is only, sir, that you would promise to hate me with as much sincerity as I will endeavour to make you a suitable return."

"I granted that request, madam, seven years before you asked it," said I, "for I heartily hated the whole sex, and scarce know how I came to abate that good disposition in compliment to your conversation; but I assure you that abatement is so little that it does no injury to your proposal."

"There's some mystery in that indeed, sir," said she, "for I desire to assist your aversion to women in a more particular manner, and hoped it should never abate under my management." We said a thousand ill-natured things after this, but she outdid me, for she had such a stock of bitterness upon her tongue as no woman ever went beyond her, and yet all this while she was the pleasantest and most obliging creature in every part of our conversation that could possibly be, and meant not one word of what she said; no, not a word. But I must confess it no way answered her end, for it really cooled all my thoughts of her, and I, that had lived in so perfect an indifferency to the sex all my days, was easily returned to that condition again, and began to grow very cold and negligent in my usual respects to her upon all occasions.

She soon found she had gone too far with me, and, in short, that she was extremely out in her politics; that she had to do with one that was not listed yet among the whining sort of lovers, and knew not what it was to adore a mistress in order to abuse her; and that it was not with me as it was with the usual sort of men in love, that are warmed by the cold, and rise in their passions as the ladies fall in their returns. On the contrary, she found that it was quite altered. I was civil to her, as before, but not so forward. When I saw her at her chamber-window, I did not throw

mine open, as I usually had done, to talk with her.
When she sung in the parlour, where I could easily
hear it, I did not listen. When she visited at the house
where I lodged, I did not always come down ; or if I
did, I had business which obliged me to go abroad ;
and yet all this while, when I did come into her company, I was as intimate as ever.

I could easily see that this madded her to the heart,
and that she was perplexed to the last degree ; for she
found that she had all her game to play over again ;
that so absolute a reservedness, even to rudeness and ill
manners, was a little too much ; but she was a mere
posture-mistress in love, and could put herself into
what shapes she pleased.

She was too wise to show a fondness or forward-
ness that looked like kindness. She knew that was the
meanest and last step a woman can take, and lays her
under the foot of the man she pretends to. Fondness
is not the last favour indeed, but it is the last favour
but one that a woman can grant, and lays her almost as
low ; I mean, it lays her at the mercy of the man she
shows it to ; but she was not come to that neither.
This chameleon put on another colour, turned, on a
sudden, the gravest, soberest, majestic madam, so that
any one would have thought she was advanced in age
in one week from two-and-twenty to fifty, and this she
carried on with so much government of herself that it
did not in the least look like art ; but if it was a representation of nature only, it was so like nature itself that
nobody living can be able to distinguish. She sung
very often in her parlour, as well by herself as with
two young ladies who came often to see her. I could
see by their books, and her guitar in her hand, that
she was singing ; but she never opened the window, as
she was wont to do. Upon my coming to my window,
she kept her own always shut ; or if it was open, she

would be sitting at work, and not look up, it may be, once in half-an-hour.

If she saw me by accident all this while, she would smile, and speak as cheerfully as ever ; but it was but a word or two, and so make her honours and be gone ; so that, in a word, we conversed just as we did after I had been there a week.

She tired me quite out at this work ; for though I began the strangeness, indeed, yet I did not design the carrying it on so far.   But she held it to the last, just in the same manner as she began it.   She came to the house where I lodged as usual, and we were often together, supped together, played at cards together, danced together ; for in France I accomplished myself with everything that was needful to make me what I believed myself to be even from a boy—I mean a gentleman.   I say, we conversed together, as above, but she was so perfectly another thing to what she used to be in every part of her conversation that it presently occurred to me that her former behaviour was a kind of a rant or fit ; that either it was the effect of some extraordinary levity that had come upon her, or that it was done to mimic the coquets of the town, believing it might take with me, who she thought was a Frenchman, and that it was what I loved.   But her new gravity was her real natural temper, and indeed it became her so much better, or, as I should say, she acted it so well, that it really brought me back to have, not as much only, but more mind to her than ever I had before.

However, it was a great while before I discovered myself, and I stayed indeed to find out, if possible, whether this change was real or counterfeit ; for I could not easily believe it was possible the gay humour she used to appear in could be a counterfeit.   It was not, therefore, till a year and almost a quarter that I came to any resolution in my thoughts about her, when, on a mere accident, we came to a little conversation together.

She came to visit at our house as usual, and it happened all the ladies were gone abroad ; but, as it fell out, I was in the passage or entry of the house, going towards the stairs, when she knocked at the door ; so, stepping back, I opened the door, and she, without any ceremony, came in, and ran forward into the parlour, supposing the women had been there. I went in after her, as I could do no less, because she did not know that the family was abroad.

Upon my coming in she asked for the ladies. I told her I hoped she came to visit me now, for that the ladies were all gone abroad. "Are they ?" said she, as if surprised—though I understood afterwards she knew it before, as also that I was at home—and then rises up to be gone. "No, madam," said I, "pray do not go ; when ladies come to visit me, I do not use to tire them of my company so soon." "That's as ill-natured," says she, "as you could possibly talk. Pray don't pretend I came to visit you. I am satisfied who I came to visit, and satisfied that you know it." "Yes, madam," said I ; "but if I happen to be all of the family that's left at home, then you came to visit me."

"I never receive visits from those that I hate," says she.

"You have me there, indeed," said I ; "but you never gave me leave to tell you why I hated you. I hated you because you would never give me an opportunity to tell you I loved you. Sure, you took me for some frightful creature, that you would never come near enough so much as to let me whisper to you that I love you."

"I never care to hear anything so disagreeable," says she, "though it be spoken ever so softly."

We rallied thus for an hour. In short, she showed the abundance of her wit, and I an abundant deficiency of mine; for though three or four times she provoked me to the last degree, so that once I was going to tel her I had enough of her company, and, if she pleased I would wait upon her to the door, yet she had always so much witchcraft on her tongue that she brought herself off again; till, to make the story short, we came at last to talk seriously on both sides about matrimony, and she heard me freely propose it, and answered me directly upon many occasions. For example, she told me I would carry her away to France or to Virginia, and that she could not think of leaving England, her native country. I told her I hoped she did not take me for a kidnapper. (By the way, I did not tell her how I had been kidnapped myself.) She said no; but the consequence of my affairs, which were, it seems, mostly abroad, might oblige me to go, and she could never think of marrying any man that she could not be content to go all over the world with, if he had occasion to go himself. This was handsomely expressed indeed. I made her easy on that point, and thus we began the grand parley; which indeed she drew me into with the utmost art and subtilty, such as was peculiar to herself, but was infinitely her advantage in our treating of marriage; for she made me effectually court her, though at the same time in her design she courted me with the utmost skill, and such skill it was that her design was perfectly impenetrable to the last moment.

In short, we came nearer and nearer every time we met; and after one casual visit more, in which I had the mighty favour of talking with her alone, I then waited on her every day at her own house, or lodgings rather, and so we set about the work to a purpose, and in about a month we gave the world the slip, and were privately married, to avoid ceremony and the public inconveniency of a wedding.

We soon found a house proper for our dwelling, and so went to housekeeping. We had not been long together but I found that gay temper of my wife returned, and she threw off the mask of her gravity and good conduct, that I had so long fancied was her mere natural disposition ; and now, having no more occasion for disguises, she resolved to seem nothing but what really she was, a wild, untamed colt, perfectly loose, and careless to conceal any part, no, not the worst of her conduct.

She carried on this air of levity to such an excess that I could not but be dissatisfied at the expense of it ; for she kept company that I did not like, lived beyond what I could support, and sometimes lost at play more than I cared to pay. Upon which, one day, I took occasion to mention it, but lightly ; and said to her, by way of raillery, that we lived merrily, for as long as it would last. She turned short upon me, "What do you mean?" says she. "Why, you don't pretend to be uneasy, do ye?" "No, no, madam, not I, by no means ; it is no business of mine, you know," said I, "to inquire what my wife spends, or whether she spends more than I can afford, or less. I only desire the favour to know, as near as you can guess, how long you will please to take to despatch me, for I would not be too long a-dying."

"I do not know what you talk of," says she. "You may die as leisurely, or as hastily, as you please, when your time comes ; I a'nt a-going to kill you, as I know of."

"But you are a-going to starve me, madam," said I, "and hunger is as leisurely a death as breaking upon the wheel."

"I starve you ! Why, are not you a great Virginia

merchant, and did not I bring you £1500? What would you have? Sure, you can maintain a wife out of that, can't you?"

"Yes, madam," says I, "I could maintain a wife, but not a gamester, though you had brought me £1500 a year; no estate is big enough for a box and dice."

She took fire at that, and flew out in a passion, and after a great many bitter words, told me, in short, that she saw no occasion to alter her conduct; and as for my not maintaining her, when I could not maintain her longer she would find some way or other to maintain herself.

Some time after the first rattle of this kind, she vouchsafed to let me know that she was pleased to be with child. I was at first glad of it, in hopes it would help to abate her madness; but it was all one, and her being with child only added to the rest, for she made such preparations for her lying-in, and the other appendixes of a child's being born, that, in short, I found she would be downright distracted. And I took the liberty to tell her one day that she would soon bring herself and me to destruction, and entreated her to consider that such figures as those were quite above us, and out of our circle; and, in short, that I neither could nor would allow such expenses; that, at this rate, two or three children would effectually ruin me, and that I desired her to consider what she was doing.

She told me, with an air of disdain, that it was none of her business to consider anything of that matter; that if I could not allow it, she would allow it herself, and I might do my worst.

I begged her to consider things for all that, and not drive me to extremities; that I married her to love and cherish her, and use her as a good wife ought to be used, but not to be ruined and undone by her. In a word, nothing could mollify her, nor any argument persuade her to moderation, but withal she took it so heinously that I should pretend to restrain her, that she told me in so many words she would drop her burthen with me, and then, if I did not like it, she would take care of herself; she would not live with me an hour, for she would not be restrained, not she; and talked a long while at that rate.

I told her, as to her child, which she called her burthen, it should be no burthen to me; as to the rest, she might do as she pleased; it might, however, do me this favour, that I should have no more lyings in at the rate of £136 at a time, as I found she intended it should be now. She told me she could not tell that; if she had no more by me, she hoped she should by somebody else. "Say you so, madam?" said I. "Then they that get them shall keep them." She did not know that neither, she said, and so turned it off jeering, and, as it were, laughing at me.

This last discourse nettled me, I must confess, and the more because I had a great deal of it and very often, till, in short, we began at length to enter into a friendly treaty about parting.

Nothing could be more criminal than the several discourses we had upon this subject. She demanded a separate maintenance, and, in particular, at the rate of £300 a year, and I demanded security of her that she should not run me in debt. She demanded the keeping of the child, with an allowance of £100 a year for that, and I demanded that I should be secured from being charged for keeping any she might have by somebody else, as she had threatened me.

In the interval, and during these contests, she dropped her burthen (as she called it), and brought me a son, a very fine child.

She was content during her lying-in to abate a

little, though it was but a very little indeed, of the
great expense she had intended, and, with some difficulty and persuasion, was content with a suit of child-
bed linen of £15 instead of one she had intended of
threescore; and this she magnified as a particular
testimony of her condescension and a yielding to my
avaricious temper, as she called it.

But after she was up again, it was the same thing,
and she went on with her humour to that degree that
in a little time she began to carry it on to other
excesses, and to have a sort of fellows come to visit
her, which I did not like, and once, in particular,
stayed abroad all night. The next day, when she
came home, she began to cry out first; told me where
(as she said) she lay, and that the occasion was a
christening, where the company had a feast and
stayed too late; that, if I was dissatisfied, I might
inform myself there of all the particulars, where she
lay, and the like. I told her coldly, "Madam, you do
well to suggest my being dissatisfied, for you may be
sure I am, and you could expect no other; that as to
going to your haunts to inform myself, that is not my
business: it is your business to bring testimonies of
your behaviour, and to prove where you lay, and in
what company. It is enough to me that you lay out of
your own house, without your husband's knowledge or
consent, and before you and I converse again I must
have some satisfaction of the particulars."

She answered, with all her heart; she was as indifferent as I; and since I took so ill her lying at a
friend's house on an extraordinary occasion, she gave
me to understand that it was what she would have me
expect, and what she would have the liberty to do
when she thought fit.

"Well, madam," said I, "if I must expect what
I cannot allow, you must expect I shall shut my

doors by day against those that keep out of them at night."

She would try me, she said, very speedily; and if I shut the doors against her, she would find a way to make me open them.

"Well, madam," says I, "you threaten me hard, but I would advise you to consider before you take such measures, for I shall be as good as my word." However, it was not long that we could live together upon these terms; for I found very quickly what company she kept, and that she took a course which I ought not to bear. So I began the separation first, and refused her my bed. We had indeed refrained all converse as husband and wife for about two months before, for I told her very plainly I would father no brats that were not of my own getting; and matters coming thus gradually to an extremity, too great to continue as it was, she went off one afternoon, and left me a line in writing, signifying that affairs had come to such a pass between us that she did not think fit to give me the opportunity of shutting her out of doors, and that therefore she had retired herself to such a place, naming a relation of her own, as scandalous as herself; and that she hoped I would not give her the trouble to sue for her support in the ordinary course of law, but that, as her occasions required, she should draw bills upon me, which she expected I would not refuse.

I was extremely satisfied with this proceeding, and took care to let her hear of it, though I gave no answer at all to her letter; and as I had taken care before that whenever she played such a prank as this, she should not be able to carry much with her, so, after she was gone, I immediately broke up house-keeping, sold my furniture by public outcry, and in it everything in particular that was her own, and set a bill upon my door, giving her to understand by it that she had passed the Rubicon, that as she had taken such a step of her own accord, so there was no room left her ever to think of coming back again.

This was what any one may believe I should not have done if I had seen any room for a reformation; but she had given me such testimonies of a mind alienated from her husband, in particular espousing her own unsufferable levity, that there was indeed no possibility of our coming afterwards to any terms again.

However, I kept a couple of trusty agents so near her that I failed not to have a full account of her conduct, though I never let her know anything of me but that I was gone over to France. As to her bills which she said she would draw upon me, she was as good as her word in drawing one of £30, which I refused to accept, and never gave her leave to trouble me with another.

It is true, and I must acknowledge it, that all this was a very melancholy scene of life to me, and but that she took care by carrying herself to the last degree provoking, and continually to insult me, I could never have gone on to the parting with so much resolution; for I really loved her very sincerely, and could have been anything but a beggar and a cuckold with her, but those were intolerable to me, especially as they were put upon me with so much insult and rudeness.

But my wife carried it at last to a point that made all things light and easy to me, for after above a year's separation, and keeping such company as she thought fit, she was pleased to be with child again, in which she had, however, so much honesty as not to pretend that she had had anything to do with me. What a wretched life she led after this, and how she brought herself to the utmost extremity of misery and distress, I may speak of hereafter.

I had found, soon after our parting, that I had a great deal of reason to put myself into a posture at first not to be imposed upon by her ; for I found very quickly that she had run herself into debt in several places very considerably, and that it was upon a supposition that I was liable to those debts. But I was gone, and it was absolutely necessary I should do so ; upon which she found herself obliged, out of her wicked gains, however, whatever she made of them, to discharge most of those debts herself.

As soon as she was delivered of her child, in which my intelligence was so good that I had gotten sufficient proof of it, I sued her in the ecclesiastical court, in order to obtain a divorce ; and as she found it impossible to avoid it, so she declined the defence, and I gained a legal decree, or what they call it, of divorce, in the usual time of such process ; and now I thought myself a free man once again, and began to be sick of wedlock with all my heart.

I lived retired, because I knew she had contracted debts which I should be obliged to pay, and I was resolved to be gone out of her reach with what speed I could. But it was necessary that I should stay till the Virginia fleet came in, because I looked for at least three hundred hogsheads of tobacco from thence, which I knew would heal all my breaches ; for indeed the extravagance of three years with this lady had sunk me most effectually, even far beyond her own fortune, which was considerable, though not quite £1500, as she had called it.

But all the mischiefs I met with on account of this match were not over yet ; for when I had been parted with her about three months, and had refused to accept her bill of £30, which I mentioned above, though I was removed from my first lodgings too, and thought I had effectually secured myself from being found out, yet there came a gentleman well dressed to my lodgings one day, and was let in before I knew of it, or else I should scarce have admitted him.

He was led into a parlour, and I came down to him in my gown and slippers. When I came into the room he called me as familiarly by my name as if he had known me twenty years, and pulling out a pocket-book, he shows me a bill upon me, drawn by my wife, which was the same bill for £30 that I had refused before.

"Sir," says I, "this bill has been presented before, and I gave my answer to it then."

"Answer, sir!" says he, with a kind of jeering, taunting air. "I do not understand what you mean by an answer; it is not a question, sir; it is a bill to be paid."

"Well, sir," says I, "it is a bill; I know that, and I gave my answer to it before."

"Sir, sir," says he very saucily, "your answer! There is no answer to a bill; it must be paid. Bills are to be paid, not to be answered. They say you are a merchant, sir; merchants always pay their bills."

I began to be angry too a little, but I did not like my man, for I found he began to be quarrelsome. However, I said, "Sir, I perceive you are not much used to presenting bills. Sir, a bill is always first presented, and presenting is a question; it is asking if I will accept or pay the bill, and then whether I say yes or no, it is an answer one way or other. After 'tis accepted, it indeed requires no more answer but payment when 'tis due. If you please to inform yourself, this is the usage which all merchants or tradesmen of any kind who have bills drawn upon them act by."

"Well, sir," says he, "and what then? What is this to the paying me the £30?"

"Why, sir," says I, "it is this to it, that I told the person that brought it I should not pay it."

" Not pay it ! " says he. " But you shall pay it ; ay, ay, you will pay it."

" She that draws it has no reason to draw any bills upon me, I am sure," said I ; " and I shall pay no bills she draws, I assure you."

Upon this he turns short upon me : " Sir, she that draws this bill is a person of too much honour to draw any bill without reason, and 'tis an affront to say so of her, and I shall expect satisfaction of you for that by itself. But first the bill, sir—the bill ; you must pay the bill, sir."

I returned as short : " Sir, I affront nobody. I know the person as well as you, I hope ; and what I have said of her is no affront. She can have no reason to draw bills upon me, for I owe her nothing."

I omit intermingling the oaths he laced his speech with, as too foul for my paper. But he told me he would make me know she had friends to stand by her, that I had abused her, and he would let me know it, and do her justice. But first I must pay his bill.

I answered, in short, I would not pay the bill, nor any bills she should draw.

With that he steps to the door and shuts it, and swore by G—d he would make me pay the bill before we parted, and laid his hand upon his sword, but did not draw it out.

I confess I was frighted to the last degree, for I had no sword ; and if I had, I must own that, though I had learned a great many good things in France to make me look like a gentleman, I had forgot the main article of learning how to use a sword, a thing so universally practised there ; and, to say more, I had been perfectly unacquainted with quarrels of this nature ; so that I was perfectly surprised when he shut the door, and knew not what to say or do.

However, as it happened, the people of the house,

hearing us pretty loud, came near the door, and made a noise in the entry to let me know they were at hand; and one of the servants, going to open the door, and finding it locked, called out to me, " Sir, for God's sake open the door! What is the matter? Shall we fetch a constable?" I made no answer, but it gave me courage; so I sat down composed in one of the chairs, and said to him, " Sir, this is not the way to make me pay the bill; you had much better be easy, and take your satisfaction another way."

He understood me of fighting, which, upon my word, was not in my thoughts; but I meant that he had better take his course at law.

" With all my heart," says he; " they say you are a gentleman, and they call you colonel. Now, if you are a gentleman, I accept your challenge, sir; and if you will walk out with me, I will take it for full payment of the bill, and will decide it as gentlemen ought to do."

" I challenge you, sir!" said I. " Not I; I made no challenge," I said. " This is not the way to make me pay a bill that I have not accepted; that is, that you had better seek your satisfaction at law."

" Law!" says he; " law! Gentlemen's law is my law. In short, sir, you shall pay me or fight me." And then, as if he had mistaken, he turns short upon me, " Nay," says he, " you shall both fight me and pay me, for I will maintain her honour;" and in saying this he bestowed about six or seven " damme's" and oaths, by way of parenthesis.

This interval delivered me effectually, for just at the words " fight me, for I will maintain her honour," the maid had brought in a constable, with three or four neighbours to assist him.

He heard them come in, and began to be a little in a rage, and asked me if I intended to mob him instead of paying; and laying his hand on his sword, told me, if any man offered to break in upon him, he would run me through the first moment, that he might have the fewer to deal with afterwards.

I told him he knew I had called for no help (believing he could not be in earnest in what he had said), and that, if anybody attempted to come in upon us, it was to prevent the mischief he threatened, and which he might see I had no weapons to resist.

Upon this the constable called, and charged us both in the king's name to open the door. I was sitting in a chair, and offered to rise. He made a motion as if he would draw, upon which I sat down again, and the door not being opened, the constable set his foot against it and came in.

"Well, sir," says my gentleman, "and what now? What's your business here?" "Nay, sir," says the constable, "you see my business. I am a peace-officer; all I have to do is to keep the peace, and I find the people of the house frightened for fear of mischief between you, and they have fetched me to prevent it." "What mischief have they supposed you should find?" says he. "I suppose," says the constable, "they were afraid you should fight." "That's because they did not know this fellow here. He never fights. They call him colonel," says he. "I suppose he might be born a colonel, for I dare say he was born a coward; he never fights; he dares not see a man. If he would have fought, he would have walked out with me, but he scorns to be brave; they would never have talked to you of fighting if they had known him. I tell you, Mr Constable, he is a coward, and a coward is a rascal;" and with that he came to me, and stroked his finger down my nose pretty hard, and laughed and mocked most horribly, as if I was a coward. Now, for aught I knew, it might be true, but I was now what they call a coward made desperate, which is one of the worst of men in the world to encounter with ; for, being in a fury, I threw my head in his face, and closing with him, threw him fairly on his back by mere strength ; and had not the constable stepped in and taken me off, I had certainly stamped him to death with my feet, for my blood was now all in a flame, and the people of the house were frighted now as much the other way, lest I should kill him, though I had no weapon at all in my hand.

The constable too reproved me in his turn ; but I said to him, "Mr Constable, do you not think I am sufficiently provoked ? Can any man bear such things as these ? I desire to know who this man is and who sent him hither."

" I am," says he, "a gentleman, and come with a bill to him for money, and he refuses to pay it." "Well," says the constable very prudently, "that is none of my business ; I am no justice of the peace to hear the cause. Be that among yourselves, but keep your hands off one another, and that is as much as I desire ; and therefore, sir," says the constable to him, "if I may advise you, seeing he will not pay the bill, and that must be decided between you as the law directs, I would have you leave it for the present and go quietly away."

He made many impertinent harangues about the bill, and insisted that it was drawn by my own wife. I said angrily, "Then it was drawn by a whore." He bullied me upon that, told me I durst not tell him so anywhere else ; so I answered, "I would very soon publish her for a whore to all the world, and cry her down ;" and thus we scolded for near half-an-hour, for I took courage when the constable was there, for I knew that he would keep us from fighting, which indeed I had no mind to, and so at length I got rid of him.

I was heartily vexed at this rencounter, and the more because I had been found out in my lodging, which I thought I had effectually concealed. However, I resolved to remove the next day, and in the meantime I kept within doors all that day till the evening, and then I went out in order not to return thither any more.

Being come out into Gracechurch Street, I observed a man follow me, with one of his legs tied up in a string, and hopping along with the other, and two crutches ; he begged for a farthing, but I inclining not to give him anything, the fellow followed me still, till I came to a court, when I answered hastily to him, " I have nothing for you !   Pray do not be so troublesome ! " with which words he knocked me down with one of his crutches.

Being stunned with the blow, I knew nothing what was done to me afterwards ; but coming to myself again, I found I was wounded very frightfully in several places, and that among the rest my nose was slit upwards, one of my ears cut almost off, and a great cut with a sword on the side of the forehead ; also a stab into the body, though not dangerous.

Who had been near me, or struck me, besides the cripple that struck me with his crutch, I knew not, nor do I know to this hour ; but I was terribly wounded, and lay bleeding on the ground some time, till, coming to myself, I got strength to cry out for help, and people coming about me, I got some hands to carry me to my lodging, where I lay by it more than two months before I was well enough to go out of doors ; and when I did go out, I had reason to believe that I was waited for by some rogues, who watched an opportunity to repeat the injury I had met with before.

This made me very uneasy, and I resolved to get myself out of danger if possible, and to go over to

France, or home, as I called it, to Virginia, so to be out of the way of villains and assassinations; for every time I stirred out here I thought I went in danger of my life; and therefore, as before, I went out at night, thinking to be concealed, so now I never went out but in open day, that I might be safe, and never without one or two servants to be my lifeguard.

But I must do my wife a piece of justice here too, and that was, that, hearing what had befallen me, she wrote me a letter, in which she treated me more decently than she had been wont to do. She said she was very sorry to hear how I had been used, and the rather because she understood it was on presenting her bill to me. She said she hoped I could not, in my worst dispositions, think so hardly of her as to believe it was done by her knowledge or consent, much less by her order or direction; that she abhorred such things, and protested, if she had the least knowledge or so much as a guess at the villains concerned, she would discover them to me. She let me know the person's name to whom she gave the bill, and where he lived, and left it to me to oblige him to discover the person who had brought it and used me so ill, and wished I might find him and bring him to justice, and have him punished with the utmost severity of the law.

I took this so kindly of my wife that I think in my conscience, had she come after it herself to see how I did, I had certainly taken her again; but she satisfied herself with the civility of another letter, and desiring me to let her know as often as I could how I was; adding that it would be infinitely to her satisfaction to hear I was recovered of the hurt I had received, and that he was hanged at Tyburn who had done it.

She used some expressions signifying, as I understood them, her affliction at our parting and her continued respect for me; but did not make any motion towards returning. Then she used some arguments to move me to pay her bills, intimating that she had brought me a large fortune, and now had nothing to subsist on, which was very severe.

I wrote her an answer to this letter, though I had not to the other, letting her know how I had been used; that I was satisfied, upon her letter, that she had no hand in it; that it was not in her nature to treat me so, who had never injured her, used any violence with her, or been the cause or desire of our parting; that, as to her bill, she could not but know how much her expensive way of living had straitened and reduced me, and would, if continued, have ruined me; that she had in less than three years spent more than as much as she brought to me, and would not abate her expensive way, though calmly entreated by me, with protestations that I could not support so great an expense, but chose rather to break up her family and go from me than to restrain herself to reasonable limits; though I used no violence with her, but entreaties and earnest persuasions, backed with good reason; letting her know how my estate was, and convincing her that it must reduce us to poverty at least; that, however, if she would recall her bill, I would send her £30, which was the sum mentioned in her bill, and, according to my ability, would not let her want, if she pleased to live within due bounds; but then I let her know also that I had a very bad account of her conduct, and that she kept company with a scandalous fellow, who I named to her; that I was loth to believe such things of her, but that, to put an entire end to the report and restore her reputation, I let her know that still, after all I heard, if she would resolve to live without restraints, within the reasonable bounds of my capacity, and treat me with the same kindness, affection, and tenderness as I always had treated her, and ever would, I was willing to receive her again, and would forget all that was past; but that, if she declined me now, it would be for ever; for if she did not accept my offer, I was resolved to stay here no longer, where I had been so ill-treated on many occasions, but was preparing to go into my own country, where I would spend my days in quiet, and in a retreat from the world.

She did not give such an answer to this as I expected; for though she thanked me for the £30, yet she insisted upon her justification in all other points; and though she did not refuse to return to me, yet she did not say she accepted it, and, in short, said little or nothing to it, only a kind of claim to a reparation of her injured reputation, and the like.

This gave me some surprise at first, for I thought, indeed, any woman in her circumstances would have been very willing to have put an end to all her miseries, and to the reproach which was upon her, by a reconciliation, especially considering she subsisted at that time but very meanly. But there was a particular reason which prevented her return, and which she could not plead to in her letter, yet was a good reason against accepting an offer which she would otherwise have been glad of; and this was, that, as I have mentioned above, she had fallen into bad company, and had prostituted her virtue to some of her flatterers, and, in short, was with child; so that she durst not venture to accept my offer.

However, as I observed above, she did not absolutely refuse it, intending (as I understood afterward) to keep the treaty of it on foot till she could drop her burthen, as she had called it before, and having been delivered privately, have accepted my proposal afterward; and, indeed, this was the most prudent step she could take, or, as we may say, the only step she

(who were preparing to fall into Italy with a great army) as much at a distance as possible, which he did by taking possession of the city of Mantua, and of most of the towns on that side, as far as the Lake De la Guarda and the river Adige.

We lay in Mantua some time, but were afterwards drawn out by order of the Count de Tesse (afterwards Marshal of France), to form the French army, till the arrival of the Duke de Vendôme, who was to command in chief. Here we had a severe campaign, *anno* 1701, having Prince Eugene of Savoy and an army of forty thousand Germans, all old soldiers, to deal with; and though the French army was more numerous than the enemy by twenty-five thousand men, yet, being on the defensive, and having so many posts to cover, not knowing exactly where the Prince of Savoy, who commanded the imperial army, would attack us, it obliged the French to keep their troops so divided and so remote from one another that the Germans pushed on their design with great success, as the histories of those times more fully relate.

I was at the action of Carpi, July 1701, where we were worsted by the Germans; indeed, were forced to quit our encampment and give up to the prince the whole river Adige, and where our regiment sustained some loss. But the enemies got little by us, and Monsieur Catinat, who commanded at that time, drew up in order of battle the next day in sight of the German army, and gave them a defiance; but they would not stir, though we offered them battle two days together; for, having gained the passage over the Adige by our quitting Rivoli, which was then useless to us, their business was done.

Finding they declined a decisive action, our generals pressed them in their quarters, and made them fight for every inch of ground they gained; and at length, in the September following, we attacked them in their intrenched posts of Chiar. Here we broke into the very heart of their camp, where we made a very terrible slaughter. But I know not by what mistake among our generals, or defect in the execution of their orders, the brigade of Normandy and our Irish Brigade, who had so bravely entered the German intrenchments, were not supported as we should have been, so that we were obliged to sustain the shock of the whole German army, and at last to quit the advantage we had gained, and that not without loss ; but, being timely reinforced by a great body of horse, the enemy were in their turn beaten off too, and driven back into their very camp. The Germans boasted of having a great victory here, and indeed, in repulsing us after we had gained their camp, they had the advantage. But had Monsieur de Tesse succoured us in time, as old Catinat said he ought to have done, with twelve thousand foot which he had with him, that day's action had put an end to the war, and Prince Eugene must have been glad to have gone back to Germany in more haste than he came, if, perhaps, we had not cut him short by the way.

But the fate of things went another way, and the Germans continued all that campaign to push forward and advance one post after another, till they beat us quite out of the Milanese.

The latter part of this campaign we made only a party war, the French, according to their volatile temper, being every day abroad, either foraging or surprising the enemy's foragers, plundering or circumventing the plunders of the other side. But they very often came short home, for the Germans had the better of them on several occasions ; and indeed so many lost their lives upon these petty encounters that I think, including those who died of distempers gotten by hard service and bad quarters, lying in the field even till the middle of December among rivers and bogs, in a country so full of canals and rivers as that part of Italy is known to be; I say, we lost more men, and so did the enemy also, than would have been lost in a general decisive battle.

The Duke of Savoy, to give him his due, pressed earnestly to put it to a day and come to a battle with Prince Eugene; but the Duke de Villeroi, Monsieur Catinat, and the Count de Tesse were all against it; and the principal reason was, that they knew the weakness of the troops, who had suffered so much on so many occasions that they were in no condition to give battle to the Germans. So after, as I say, about three months' harassing one another with parties, we went into winter quarters.

Before we marched out of the field, our regiment, with a detachment of dragoons of six hundred, and about two hundred and fifty horse, went out with a design to intercept Prince Commercy, a general of note under Prince Eugene of Savoy. The detachment was intended to be only horse and dragoons; but because it was the imperialists' good luck to beat many of our parties, and, as was given out, many more than we beat of theirs, and because it was believed that the prince, who was an officer of good note among them, would not go abroad but in very good company, the Irish regiment of foot was ordered to be added, that, if possible, they might meet with their match.

I was commanded, about two hours before, to pass about two hundred foot and fifty dragoons at a small wood where our general had intelligence that prince would post some men to secure his passage, which accordingly I did. But Count Tesse, not thinking our party strong enough, had marched himself, with a thousand horse and three hundred grenadiers, to support us. And it was very well he did so; for Prince Commercy, having intelligence of the first party, came forward sooner than they expected, and fell upon them, and had entirely routed them had not the Count, hearing the firing, advanced with the thousand horse he had, with such expedition as to support his men in the very heat of the action, by which means the Germans were defeated and forced to retire. But the prince made a pretty good retreat, and after the action came on to the wood where I was posted; but the surprise of his defeat had prevented his sending a detachment to secure the pass at the wood, as he intended.

The Count de Tesse, understanding that we were sent, as above, to the wood, followed them close at the heels, to prevent our being cut off, and, if it were possible that we should give them any check at the wood, to fall in and have another brush with them. It was near night before they came to the wood, by which means they could not discern our number. But when they came up to the wood, fifty dragoons advanced to discover the pass and see if all was clear. These we suffered to pass a great way into the defile, or lane, that went through the wood, and then clapping in between them and the entrance, cut off their retreat so effectually that when they discovered us and fired, they were instantly surrounded and cut in pieces, the officers who commanded them and eight dragoons only being made prisoners.

This made the prince halt, not knowing what the case was or how strong we were, and, to get better intelligence, sent two hundred horse to surround or skirt the wood and beat up our quarter, and in the interim the Count de Tesse appeared in his rear. We found the strait he was in by the noise of our own troops at a distance; so we resolved to engage the two hundred horse immediately. Accordingly our little troop of horse drew up in the entrance of the lane and offered to skirmish, and our foot, lying behind the hedge which went round the wood, stood ready to act as occasion should offer. The horse, being attacked, gave way, and retired into the lane; but the Germans were too old for us there. They contented themselves to push us to the entrance, but would not be drawn into a narrow pass without knowing whether the hedges were lined or no.

But the prince, finding the French in his rear, and not being strong enough to engage again, resolved to force his way through, and commanded his dragoons to alight and enter the wood, to clear the hedges on either side the lane, that he might pass with his cavalry. This they did so vigorously, and were so much too strong for us, that though we made good our ground a long time, yet our men were almost half of them cut in pieces. However, we gave time to the French cavalry to come up, and to fall on the prince's troops and cut them off, and take a great many prisoners, and then we retreated in our turn, opening a gap for our own horse to break in. Three hundred of the dragoons were killed, and two hundred of them taken prisoners.

In the first heat of this action, a German officer of dragoons, well followed, had knocked down three men that stood next me; and, offering me quarter, I was obliged to accept it, and gave him my sword; for our men were upon the point of quitting their post and shifting every one as they could. But the scale was turned, for our cavalry breaking in, as above, the dragoons went to wreck, and the officer who had me prisoner, turning to me, said, "We are all lost." I asked him if I could serve him. "Stand still a little," says he; for his men fought most desperately indeed. But about two hundred French horse appearing in his rear too, he said to me in French, "I will be your prisoner," and

II.

D

returning me my sword, gave me also his own. A dragoon that stood near him was just going to do the like, when he was shot dead, and the horse coming up, the field was cleared in an instant. But Prince Commercy went off with the rest of his party, and was pursued no farther.

There were sixteen or seventeen of our men released, as I was, from being taken; but they had not the luck I had, to take the officer that had them in keeping. He had been so generous to me as not to ask what money I had about me, though I had not much if he had. But I lost by his civility, for then I could not have the assurance to ask him for his money, though I understood he had near a hundred pistoles about him. But he very handsomely at night, when we came to our tents, made me a present of twenty pistoles, and in return I obtained leave for him to go to Prince Eugene's camp upon his parole, which he did, and so got himself exchanged.

It was after this campaign that I was quartered at Cremona, when the action happened there of which I have spoken already, and where our Irish regiment did such service that they saved the town from being really surprised, and indeed beat the Germans out again, after they had been masters of three-quarters of the town six hours, and by which they gained a very great reputation.

But I hasten on to my own history, for I am not writing a journal of the wars, in which I had no long share.

The summer after this our two Irish regiments were drawn out into the field, and had many a sore brush with the Germans; for Prince Eugene, a vigilant general, gave us little rest, and gained many advantages by his continual moving up and down, harassing his own men and ours too; and whoever will do the

French justice, and knew how they had behaved, must acknowledge they never declined the Germans, but fought them upon all occasions with the utmost resolution and courage; and though it cost the blood of an infinite number of fine gentlemen, as well as private soldiers, yet the Duke de Vendôme, who now commanded, though King Philip was himself in the army this campaign, made the Prince of Savoy a full return in his own kind, and drove him from post to post, till he was just at the point of quitting the whole country of Italy. All that gallant army Prince Eugene brought with him into Italy, which was the best without doubt, for the goodness of the troops, that ever were there, laid their bones in that country, and many thousands more after them, till, the affairs of France declining in other places, they were forced in their turn to give way to their fate, as may be seen in the histories of those times, as above. But it is none of my business.

The part that I bore in these affairs was but short and sharp. We took the field about the beginning of July 1702, and the Duke de Vendôme ordered the whole army to draw the sooner together, in order to relieve the city of Mantua, which was blocked up by the imperialists.

Prince Eugene was a politic, and indeed a fortunate, prince, and had the year before pushed our army upon many occasions. But his good fortune began to fail him a little this year, for our army was not only more numerous than his, but the duke was in the field before him; and as the prince had held Mantua closely blocked up all the winter, the duke resolved to relieve the town, cost what it would. As I said, the duke was first in the field; the prince was in no condition to prevent his raising the blockade by force; so he drew off his troops, and leaving several strong bodies of troops to protect Bersello, which the Duke de Vendôme threatened, and Borgo Fort, where his magazine lay, he drew all the rest of his forces together, to make head against us.  By this time the king of Spain was come into the army, and the Duke de Vendôme lay with about thirty-five thousand men near Luzara, which he had resolved to attack, to bring Prince Eugene to a battle.  The Prince of Vaudemont lay intrenched with twenty thousand more at Rivalto, behind Mantua, to cover the frontiers of Milan, and there was near twelve thousand in Mantua itself; and Monsieur Pracontal lay with ten thousand men just under the cannon of one of the forts which guard the causeway which leads into the city of Mantua; so that, had all these joined, as they would have done in a few days more, the prince must have been put to his shifts, and would have had enough to do to have maintained himself in Italy; for he was master of no one place in the country that could have held out a formal siege of fifteen days' open trenches, and he knew all this very well; and therefore it seems, while the Duke of Vendôme resolved, if possible, to bring him to a battle, and to that end made dispositions to attack Luzara, we were surprised to find, the 15th of June 1702, the whole imperial army appeared in *battalia*, and in full march, to attack us.

As it happened, our army was all marching in columns towards them, as we had done for two days before; and I should have told you that, three days before, the duke having noticed that General Visconti, with three imperial regiments of horse and one of dragoons, was posted at San-Victoria, on the Tessona, he resolved to attack them; and this design was carried so secretly, that while Monsieur Visconti, though our army was three leagues another way, was passing towards the Modenese, he found himself unexpectedly attacked by six thousand horse and dragoons of the

French army. He defended himself very bravely for near an hour; when, being overpowered, and finding he should be forced into disorder, he sounded a retreat. But the squadrons had not faced about to make their retreat scarce a quarter of an hour, when they found themselves surrounded with a great body of infantry, who had entirely cut off their retreat, except over the bridge of Tessona, which being thronged with their baggage, they could neither get backward or forward; so they thrust and tumbled over one another in such a manner that they could preserve no kind of order; but abundance fell into the river and were drowned, many were killed, and more taken prisoners; so that, in a word, the whole three regiments of horse and one of dragoons were entirely defeated.

This was a great blow to the prince, because they were some of the choicest troops of his whole army. We took about four hundred prisoners, and all their baggage, which was a very considerable booty, and about eight hundred horses; and no doubt these troops were very much wanted in the battle that ensued on the 15th, as I have said. Our army being in full march, as above, to attack Luzara, a party of Germans appeared, being about six hundred horse, and in less than an hour more their whole army, in order of battle.

Our army formed immediately, and the duke posted the regiments as they came up so much to their advantage that Prince Eugene was obliged to alter his dispositions, and had this particular inconvenience upon his hands, viz., to attack an army superior to his own, in all their most advantageous posts; whereas, had he thought fit to have waited but one day, we should have met him half-way. But this was owing to the pride of the German generals, and their being so opinionated of the goodness of their troops. The royal army was posted with the left to the great river

Po, on the other side of which the Prince of Vaudemont's army lay cannonading the intrenchments which the imperialists had made at Borgo Fort; and hearing that there was like to be a general battle, he detached twelve battalions and about a thousand horse, to reinforce the royal army; all which, to our great encouragement, had time to join the army, while Prince Eugene was making his new dispositions for the attack. And yet it was the coming of these troops which caused Prince Eugene to resolve to begin the fight, expecting to have come to an action before they could come up. But he was disappointed in the reason of fighting, and yet was obliged to fight too, which was an error in the prince that it was too late to retrieve.

It was five o'clock in the evening before he could bring up his whole line to engage; and then, after having cannonaded us to no great purpose for half-an-hour, his right, commanded by the Prince de Commercy, attacked our left wing with great fury. Our men received them so well and seconded one another so punctually that they were repulsed with a very great slaughter; and the Prince de Commercy being, unhappily for them, killed in the first onset, the regiments, for want of orders, and surprised with the fall of so great a man, were pushed into disorder, and one whole brigade was entirely broke.

But their second line, advancing under General Herbeville, restored things in the first. The battalions rallied, and they came boldly on to charge a second time, and being seconded with new reinforcements from their main body, our men had their turn, and were pushed to a canal which lay on their left flank between them and the Po, behind which they rallied; and being supported by new troops, as well horse as foot, they fought on both sides with the utmost obstinacy, and with such courage and skill that it was not possible to judge who should have had the better could they have been able to have fought it out.

On the right of the royal army was posted the flower of the French cavalry—namely, the gendarmes, the royal carbineers, and the queen's horse-guards, with four hundred horse more—and next them the infantry, among which were our brigade. The horse advanced first to charge, and they carried all before them sword in hand, receiving the fire of two imperial regiments of cuirassiers without firing a shot, and falling in among them, bore them down by the strength of their horses, putting them into confusion, and left so clear a field for us to follow that the first line of our infantry stood drawn up upon the ground which the enemy at first possessed.

In this first attack the Marquis de Crequi, who commanded the whole right wing, was killed—a loss which fully balanced the death of the Prince de Commercy on the side of the Germans. After we had thus pushed the enemy's cavalry, as above, their troops, being rallied by the dexterity of their generals and supported by three imperial regiments of foot, came on again to the charge with such fury that nothing could withstand them. And here two battalions of our Irish regiments were put into disorder, and abundance of our men killed ; and here also I had the misfortune to receive a musket-shot, which broke my left arm ; and that was not all, for I was knocked down by a giant-like German soldier, who, when he thought he had killed me, set his foot upon me, but was immediately shot dead by one of my men, and fell just upon me, which, my arm being broken, was a very great mischief to me ; for the very weight of the fellow, who was almost as big as a horse, was such that I was not able to stir.

Our men were beaten back after this from the place where they stood ; and so I was left in possession of the enemy, but was not their prisoner—that is to say, was not found till next morning, when a party being sent, as usual, with surgeons to look after the wounded men among the dead, found me almost smothered with the dead Germans and others that lay near me. However, to do them justice, they used me with humanity, and the surgeons set my arm very skilfully and well ; and four or five days after, I had liberty to go to Parma upon parole.

Both the armies continued fighting, especially on our left, till it was so dark that it was impossible to know who they fired at, or for the generals to see what they did ; so they abated firing gradually, and, as it may be truly said, the night parted them.

Both sides claimed the victory, and both concealed their losses as much as it was possible ; but it is certain that never battle was fought with greater bravery and obstinacy than this was ; and had there been daylight to have fought it out, doubtless there would have been many thousand more men killed on both sides.

All the Germans had to entitle them to the victory was, that they made our left retire, as I have said, to the canal, and to the high banks or mounds on the edge of the Po ; but they had so much advantage in the retreat—they fired from thence among the thickest of the enemy, and could never be forced from their posts.

The best testimony the royal army had of the victory, and which was certainly the better of the two, was, that, two days after the fight, they attacked Guastalia, as it were in view of the German army, and forced the garrison to surrender, and to swear not to serve again for six months, which, they being fifteen hundred men, was a great loss to the Germans ; and

the field that I could not dispense with it; but an intervening accident made that part easy to me. The war was now renewed between France and England and Holland, just as it was before; and the French king, meditating nothing more than how to give the English a diversion, fitted out a strong squadron of men-of-war and frigates at Dunkirk, on board of which he embarked a body of troops of about six thousand five hundred men, besides volunteers; and the new king, as we called him, though more generally he was called the Chevalier de St George, was shipped along with them, and all for Scotland.

I pretended a great deal of zeal for this service, and that if I might be permitted to sell my company in the Irish regiment I was in, and have the chevalier's brevet for a colonel, in case of raising troops for him in Great Britain after his arrival, I would embark volunteer and serve at my own expense. The latter gave me a great advantage with the chevalier; for now I was esteemed as a man of consideration, and one that must have a considerable interest in my own country. So I obtained leave to sell my company, and having had a good round sum of money remitted me from London, by the way of Holland, I prepared a very handsome equipage, and away I went to Dunkirk to embark.

I was very well received by the chevalier; and as he had an account that I was an officer in the Irish brigade, and had served in Italy, and consequently was an old soldier, all this added to the character which I had before, and made me have a great deal of honour paid me, though at the same time I had no particular attachment to his person or to his cause. Nor indeed did I much consider the cause of one side or other. If I had, I should hardly have risked, not my life only, but effects too, which were all, as I might say, from that moment forfeited to the English government, and were too evidently in their power to confiscate at their pleasure.

However, having just received a remittance from London of £300 sterling, and sold my company in the Irish regiment for very near as much, I was not only insensibly drawn in, but was perfectly volunteer in that dull cause, and away I went with them at all hazards. It belongs very little to my history to give an account of that fruitless expedition, only to tell you that, being so closely and effectually chased by the English fleet, which was superior in force to the French, I may say that, in escaping them, I escaped being hanged.

It was the good fortune of the French that they overshot the port they aimed at, and intending for the Frith of Forth, or, as it is called, the Frith of Edinburgh, the first land they made was as far north as a place called Montrose, where it was not their business to land, and so they were obliged to come back to the frith, and were gotten to the entrance of it, and came to an anchor for the tide. But this delay or hindrance gave time to the English, under Sir George Byng, to come to the frith, and they came to an anchor, just as we did, only waiting to go up the frith with the flood.

Had we not overshot the port, as above, all our squadron had been destroyed in two days, and all we could have done had been to have gotten into the pier or haven at Leith with the smaller frigates, and have landed the troops and ammunition; but we must have set fire to the men-of-war, for the English squadron was not above twenty-four hours behind us, or thereabout.

Upon this surprise, the French admiral set sail from the north point of the frith where we lay, and crowding away to the north, got the start of the English fleet, and made their escape, with the loss of one ship only, which, being behind the rest, could not get away.

When we were satisfied the English left chasing us, which was not till the third night, when we altered our course and lost sight of them, we stood over to the coast of Norway, and keeping that shore on board all the way to the mouth of the Baltic, we came to an anchor again, and sent two scouts abroad to learn news, to see if the sea was clear ; and being satisfied that the enemy did not chase us, we kept on with an easier sail, and came all back again to Dunkirk ; and glad I was to set my foot on shore again ; for all the while we were thus flying for our lives I was under the greatest terror imaginable, and nothing but halters and gibbets run in my head, concluding that, if I had been taken, I should certainly have been hanged.

But the care was now over. I took my leave of the chevalier, and of the army, and made haste to Paris. I came so unexpectedly to Paris, and to my own lodgings, that it was my misfortune to make a discovery relating to my wife which was not at all to my satisfaction ; for I found her ladyship had kept some company that I had reason to believe were not such as an honest woman ought to have conversed with, and as I knew her temper by what I had found of her myself, I grew very jealous and uneasy about her. I must own it touched me very nearly, for I began to have an extraordinary value for her, and her behaviour was very taking, especially after I had brought her into France ; but having a vein of levity, it was impossible to prevent her running into such things in a town so full of what they call gallantry as Paris.

It vexed me also to think that it should be my fate to be a cuckold both abroad and at home, and sometimes I would be in such a rage about it that I had no government of myself when I thought of it. Whole days, and I may say sometimes whole nights, I spent musing and considering what I should do to her, and especially what I should do to the villain, whoever he was, that had thus abused and supplanted me. Here indeed I committed murder more than once, or indeed than a hundred times, in my imagination ; and, as the devil is certainly an apparent prompter to wickedness, if he is not the first mover of it in our minds, he teased me night and day with proposals to kill my wife.

This horrid project he carried up so high, by raising fierce thoughts and fomenting the blood upon my contemplation of the word cuckold, that, in short, I left debating whether I should murder her or no, as a thing out of the question, and determined ; and my thoughts were then taken up only with the management how I should kill her, and how to make my escape after I had done it.

All this while I had no sufficient evidence of her guilt, neither had I so much as charged her with it or let her know I suspected her, otherwise than as she might perceive it in my conduct, and in the change of my behaviour to her, which was such that she could not but perceive that something troubled me. Yet she took no notice of it to me, but received me very well, and showed herself to be glad of my return. Nor did I find she had been extravagant in her expenses while I was abroad. But jealousy, as the wise man says, is the wrath of a man ; her being so good a hussy at what money I had left her gave my distempered fancy an opinion that she had been maintained by other people, and so had had no occasion to spend.

I must confess she had a difficult point here upon her, though she had been really honest ; for, as my head was prepossessed of her dishonesty, if she had been lavish I should have said she had spent it upon her gentlemen ; and as she had been frugal, I said she had been maintained by them. Thus, I say, my head was distempered; I believed myself abused, and nothing could put it out of my thoughts night or day.

All this while it was not visibly broken out between us; but I was so fully possessed with the belief of it that I seemed to want no evidence, and I looked with an evil eye upon everybody that came near her or that she conversed with. There was an officer of the Guards du Corps that lodged in the same house with us, a very honest gentleman and a man of quality. I happened to be in a little drawing-room adjoining to a parlour where my wife sat at that time, and this gentleman came into the parlour, which, as he was one of the family, he might have done without offence; but he, not knowing that I was in the drawing-room, sat down and talked with my wife. I heard every word they said, for the door between us was open; nor could I say that there passed anything between them but cursory discourse. They talked of casual things, of a young lady, a burgher's daughter of nineteen, that had been married the week before to an advocate in the Parliament of Paris, vastly rich, and about sixty-three; and of another, a widow lady of fortune in Paris, that had married her deceased husband's *valet de chambre;* and of such casual matters, that I could find no fault with her now at all.

But it filled my head with jealous thoughts and fired my temper. Now I fancied he used too much freedom with her, then that she used too much freedom to him, and once or twice I was upon the point of breaking in upon them and affronting them both, but I restrained myself. At length he talked something merrily of the lady throwing away her maidenhead, as I understood it, upon an old man; but still it was nothing indecent. But I, who was all on fire already, could bear it no longer, but started up and came into the room, and catching at my wife's words, "Say you so, madam?"

said I. "Was he too old for her?" and giving the officer a look that I fancy was something akin to the face on the sign called the Bull and Mouth, within Aldersgate, I went out into the street.

The marquis—so he was styled—a man of honour and of spirit too, took it as I meant it, and followed me in a moment and "hemmed" after me in the street; upon which I stopped, and he came up to me. "Sir," said he, "our circumstances are very unhappy in France, that we cannot do ourselves justice here without the most severe treatment in the world. But, come on it what will, you must explain yourself to me on the subject of your behaviour just now."

I was a little cooled as to the point of my conduct to him in the very few moments that had passed, and was very sensible that I was wrong to him; and I said, therefore, to him, very frankly, "Sir, you are a gentleman whom I know very well, and I have a very great respect for you; but I had been disturbed a little about the conduct of my wife, and were it your own case, what would you have done less?"

"I am sorry for any dislike between you and your wife," says he; "but what is that to me? Can you charge me with any indecency to her, except my talking so and so?" (at which he repeated the words); "and as I knew you were in the next room and heard every word, and that all the doors were open, I thought no man could have taken amiss so innocent an expression."

"I could no otherwise take it amiss," said I, "than as I thought it implied a farther familiarity, and that you cannot expect should be borne by any man of honour. However, sir," said I, "I spoke only to my wife. I said nothing to you, but gave you my hat as I passed you."

"Yes," said he, "and a look as full of rage as the devil. Are there no words in such looks?"

"I can say nothing to that," said I, "for I cannot see my own countenance; but my rage, as you call it, was at my wife, not at you."

"But hark you, sir," said he, growing warm as I grew calm, "your anger at your wife was for her discourse with me, and I think that concerns me too, and I ought to resent it."

"I think not, sir," said I; "nor, had I found you in bed with my wife, would I have quarrelled with you; for if my wife will let you lie with her, it is she is the offender. What have I to do with you? You could not lie with her if she was not willing; and if she is willing to be a whore, I ought to punish her; but I should have no quarrel with you. I will lie with your wife if I can, and then I am even with you."

I spoke this all in good humour and in order to pacify him, but it would not do; but he would have me give him satisfaction, as he called it. I told him I was a stranger in the country, and perhaps should find little mercy in their course of justice; that it was not my business to fight any man in his vindicating his keeping company with my wife, for that the injury was mine, in having a bad woman to deal with; that there was no reason in the thing, that after any man should have found the way into my bed, I, who am injured, should go and stake my life upon an equal hazard against the man who has abused me.

Nothing would prevail with this person to be quiet for all this; but I had affronted him, and no satisfaction could be made him but that at the point of the sword; so we agreed to go away together to Lisle, in Flanders. I was now soldier enough not to be afraid to look a man in the face, and as the rage at my wife inspired me with courage, so he let fall a word that fired and provoked me beyond all patience; for, speaking of the distrust I had of my wife, he said, unless I had good information I ought not to suspect my wife. I told him, if I had good information, I should be past suspicion. He replied, if he was the happy man, that had so much of her favour, he would take care then to put me past the suspicion. I gave him as rough an answer as he could desire, and he returned in French, "*Nous verrons à Lisle;*" that is to say, "We will talk further of it at Lisle."

I told him I did not see the benefit either to him or me of going so far as Lisle to decide this quarrel, since now I perceived he was the man I wanted; that we might decide this quarrel *au champ*, upon the spot, and whoever had the fortune to fall the other might make his escape to Lisle as well afterwards as before.

Thus we walked on talking very ill-naturedly on both sides, and yet very mannerly, till we came clear of the suburbs of Paris, on the way to Charenton; when, seeing the way clear, I told him under those trees was a very fit place for us, pointing to a row of trees adjoining to Monsieur ——'s garden-wall. So we went thither, and fell to work immediately. After some fencing he made a home-thrust at me, and run me into my arm, a long slanting wound, but at the same time received my point into his body, and soon after fell. He spoke some words before he dropped: first he told me I had killed him; then he said he had indeed wronged me, and as he knew it, he ought not to have fought me. He desired I would make my escape immediately, which I did into the city, but no farther, nobody, as I thought, having seen us together. In the afternoon, about six hours after the action, messengers brought news, one on the heels of another, that the marquis was mortally wounded, and carried into a house at Charenton. That account, saying he was not dead, surprised me a little, not doubting but that, concluding I had made my escape, he would own who it was. However, I discovered nothing of my concern, but, going up into my chamber, I took out of a cabinet there what money I had, which indeed was so much as I thought would be sufficient for my expenses. But having an accepted bill for two thousand livres, I walked sedately to a merchant who knew me, and got fifty pistoles of him upon my bill, letting him know my business called me to England, and I would take the rest of him when he had received it.

Having furnished myself thus, I provided me a horse for my servant, for I had one very good one of my own, and once more ventured home to my lodging, where I heard again that the marquis was not dead. My wife all this while covered her concern for the marquis so well that she gave me no room to make any remark upon her; but she saw evidently the marks of rage and deep resentment in my behaviour after some little stay, and perceiving me making preparation for a journey, she said to me, "Are you going out of town?" "Yes, madam," says I, "that you may have room to mourn for your friend the marquis;" at which she started, and showed she was indeed in a most terrible fright, and making a thousand crosses about herself, with a great many callings upon the Blessed Virgin and her country saints, she burst out at last, "Is it possible? Are you the man that has killed the marquis? Then you are undone, and I too."

"You may, madam, be a loser by the marquis being killed; but I'll take care to be as little a loser by you as I can. 'Tis enough; the marquis has honestly confessed your guilt, and I have done with you." She would have thrown herself into my arms, protesting her innocence, and told me she would fly with me, and would convince me of her fidelity by such testimonies as I could not but be satisfied with, but I thrust her violently from me. *"Allez, infame!"* said I. "Go, infamous creature, and take from me the necessity I should be under, if I stayed, of sending you to keep company with your dear friend the marquis." I thrust her away with such force that she fell backward upon the floor, and cried out most terribly, and indeed she had reason, for she was very much hurt.

It grieved me indeed to have thrust her away with such force, but you must consider me now in the circumstances of a man enraged, and, as it were, out of himself, furious and mad. However, I took her up from the floor and laid her on the bed, and calling up her maid, bid her go and take care of her mistress; and, going soon after out of doors, I took horse and made the best of my way, not towards Calais or Dunkirk, or towards Flanders, whither it might be suggested I was fled, and whither they did pursue me the same evening, but I took the direct road for Lorraine, and riding all night and very hard, I passed the Maine the next day at night, at Chalons, and came safe into the Duke of Lorraine's dominions the third day, where I rested one day only to consider what course to take; for it was still a most difficult thing to pass any way, but that I should either be in the king of France's dominions or be taken by the French allies as a subject of France. But getting good advice from a priest at Bar le Duc, who, though I did not tell him the particulars of my case, yet guessed how it was, it being, as he said, very usual for gentlemen in my circumstances to fly that way;—upon this supposition, this kind *padre* got me a church pass; that is to say, he made me a purveyor for the abbey of——, and, as such, got me a passport to go to Deux Ponts, which belonged to the king of Sweden. Having such authority there, and the priest's recommendation to an ecclesiastic in the place, I got passports from thence in the king of

Sweden's name to Cologne, and then I was thoroughly
safe.    So, making my way to the Netherlands without
any difficulty, I came to the Hague, and from thence,
though very privately and by several names, I came to
England.    And thus I got clear of my Italian wife—
whore I should have called her; for, after I had made
her so myself, how should I expect any other of her?

Being arrived at London, I wrote to my friend at
Paris, but dated my letters from the Hague, where I
ordered him to direct his answers.    The chief business
of my writing was to know if my bill was paid him,
to inquire if any pursuit was made after me, and what
other news he had about me or my wife, and particularly
how it had fared with the marquis.

I received an answer in a few days, importing that
he had received the money on my bill, which he was
ready to pay as I should direct; that the marquis was
not dead; "but," said he, "you have killed him another
way, for he has lost his commission in the Guards, which
was worth to him twenty thousand livres, and he is yet a
close prisoner in the Bastile;" that pursuit was ordered
after me upon suspicion; that they had followed me to
Amiens, on the road to Dunkirk, and to Chastean de
Cambresis, on the way to Flanders, but missing me
that way, had given it over; that the marquis had been
too well instructed to own that he had fought with
me, but said that he was assaulted on the road, and
unless I could be taken, he would take his trial and
come off for want of proof; that my flying was a
circumstance indeed that moved strongly against him,
because it was known that we had had some words
that day, and were seen to walk together, but that,
nothing being proved on either side, he would come off
with the loss of his commission, which, however, being
very rich, he could bear well enough.

As to my wife, he wrote me word she was inconsolable, and had cried herself to death almost; but he added (very ill-natured indeed), whether it was for me or for the marquis, that he could not determine. He likewise told me she was in very bad circumstances and very low, so that, if I did not take some care of her, she would come to be in very great distress.

The latter part of this story moved me indeed, for I thought, however it was, I ought not to let her starve; and, besides, poverty was a temptation which a woman could not easily withstand, and I ought not to be the instrument to drive her to a horrid necessity of crime, if I could prevent it.

Upon this I wrote to him again to go to her, and talk with her, and learn as much as he could of her particular circumstances; and that, if he found she was really in want, and, particularly, that she did not live a scandalous life, he should give her twenty pistoles, and tell her, if she would engage to live retired and honestly, she should have so much annually, which was enough to subsist her.

She took the first twenty pistoles, but bade him tell me that I had wronged her and unjustly charged her, and I ought to do her justice; and I had ruined her by exposing her in such a manner as I had, having no proof of my charge or ground for any suspicion; that, as to twenty pistoles a year, it was a mean allowance to a wife that had travelled over the world, as she had done with me, and the like; and so expostulated with him to obtain forty pistoles a year of me, which I consented to. But she never gave me the trouble of paying above one year; for after that the marquis was so fond of her again that he took her away to himself, and, as my friend wrote me word, had settled four hundred crowns a year on her, and I never heard any more of her.

I was now in London, but was obliged to be very

retired and change my name, letting nobody in the nation know who I was, except my merchant by whom I corresponded with my people in Virginia; and particularly with my tutor, who was now become the head manager of my affairs, and was in very good circumstances himself also by my means. But he deserved all I did or could do for him, for he was a most faithful friend, as well as servant, as ever man had, in that country at least.

I was not the easiest man alive, in the retired, solitary manner I now lived in; and I experienced the truth of the text, that " it is not good for man to be alone," for I was extremely melancholy and heavy, and indeed knew not what to do with myself, particularly because I was under some restraint, that I was too afraid to go abroad. At last I resolved to go quite away, and go to Virginia again, and there live retired as I could.

But when I came to consider that part more narrowly, I could not prevail with myself to live a private life. I had got a wandering kind of taste, and knowledge of things begat a desire of increasing it, and an exceeding delight I had in it, though I had nothing to do in the armies or in war, and did not design ever to meddle with it again. Yet I could not live in the world and not inquire what was doing in it; nor could I think of living in Virginia, where I was to hear my news twice a year, and read the public accounts of what was just then upon the stocks, as the history of things past.

This was my notion: I was now in my native country, where my circumstances were easy, and though I had ill-luck abroad, for I brought little money home with me, yet, by a little good management, I might soon have money by me. I had nobody to keep but myself, and my plantations in Virginia

generally returned me from £400 to £600 a year,
one year above £700, and to go thither, I concluded,
was to be buried alive; so I put off all thoughts of it,
and resolved to settle somewhere in England where I
might know everybody and nobody know me. I was
not long in concluding where to pitch, for as I spoke
the French tongue perfectly well, having been so many
years among them, it was easy for me to pass for a
Frenchman. So I went to Canterbury, called myself
an Englishman among the French, and a Frenchman
among the English; and on that score was the more
perfectly concealed, going by the name of Monsieur
Charnot with the French, and was called Mr Charnock
among the English.

Here indeed I lived perfectly incog. I made no
particular acquaintance so as to be intimate, and yet
I knew everybody, and everybody knew me. I discoursed in common, talked French with the Walloons,
and English with the English; and lived retired and
sober, and was well enough received by all sorts; but
as I meddled with nobody's business, so nobody meddled
with mine; I thought I lived pretty well.

But I was not fully satisfied. A settled family life
was the thing I loved; had made two pushes at it, as
you have heard, but with ill-success; yet the mis-
carriage of what was past did not discourage me at
all, but I resolved to marry. I looked out for a woman
as suitable as I could, but always found something or
other to shock my fancy, except once a gentleman's
daughter of good fashion; but I met with so many
repulses of one kind or another that I was forced to
give it over; and indeed, though I might be said to be
a lover in this suit, and had managed myself so well
with the young lady that I had no difficulty left but
what would soon have been adjusted, yet her father
was so difficult, made so many objections, was to-day

not pleased one way, to-morrow another, that he would stand by nothing that he himself had proposed, nor could he be ever brought to be of the same mind two days together; so that we at last put an end to the pretensions, for she would not marry without her father's consent, and I would not steal her, and so that affair ended.

I cannot say but I was a little vexed at the disappointment of this, so I left the city of Canterbury and went to London in the stage-coach. Here I had an odd scene presented as ever happened of its kind.

There was in the stage-coach a young woman and her maid. She was sitting in a very melancholy posture, for she was in the coach before me, and sighed most dreadfully all the way, and whenever her maid spoke to her she burst out into tears. I was not long in the coach with her but, seeing she made such a dismal figure, I offered to comfort her a little, and inquired into the occasion of her affliction. But she would not speak a word; but her maid, with a force of crying too, said her master was dead, at which word the lady burst out again into a passion of crying, and between mistress and maid this was all I could get for the morning part of that day. When we came to dine, I offered the lady, that seeing, I supposed, she would not dine with the company, if she would please to dine with me, I would dine in a separate room; for the rest of the company were foreigners. Her maid thanked me in her mistress's name, but her mistress could eat nothing, and desired to be private.

Here, however, I had some discourse with the maid, from whom I learned that the lady was wife to a captain of a ship, who was outward bound to somewhere in the Straits—I think it was to Zante and Venice; that, being gone no farther than the Downs, he was taken sick, and after about ten days' illness had died at Deal;

that his wife, hearing of his sickness, had gone to Deal to see him, and had come but just time enough to see him die; had stayed there to bury him, and was now coming to London in a sad, disconsolate condition indeed.

I heartily pitied the young gentlewoman indeed, and said some things to her in the coach to let her know I did so, which she gave no answer to, but in civility now and then made a bow, but never gave me the least opportunity to see her face, or so much as to know whether she had a face or no, much less to guess what form of a face it was. It was winter-time, and the coach put up at Rochester, not going through in a day, as was usual in summer; and a little before we came to Rochester I told the lady I understood she had ate nothing to-day, that such a course would but make her sick, and, doing her harm, could do her deceased husband no good; and therefore I entreated her that, as I was a stranger, and only offered a civility to her in order to abate her severely afflicting herself, she would yield so far to matters of ceremony as let us sup together as passengers; for, as to the strangers, they did not seem to understand the custom or to desire it.

She bowed, but gave no answer; only, after pressing her by arguments, which she could not deny was very civil and kind, she returned, she gave me thanks, but she could not eat. "Well, madam," said I, "do but sit down; though you think you cannot eat, perhaps you may eat a bit. Indeed you must eat, or you will destroy yourself at this rate of living, and upon the road too; in a word, you will be sick indeed." I argued with her. The maid put in, and said, "Do, madam; pray try to divert yourself a little." I pressed her again, and she bowed to me very respectfully, but still said, "No," and she could not eat. The maid continued to importune her, and said, "Dear madam, do. The gentleman is a civil gentleman; pray, madam, do;" and then, turning to me, said, "My mistress will, sir, I hope," and seemed pleased, and indeed was so.

However, I went on to persuade her; and, taking no notice of what her maid said, that I was a civil gentleman, I told her, "I am a stranger to you, madam; but if I thought you were shy of me on any account, as to civility, I will send my supper up to you in your own chamber, and stay below myself." She bowed then to me twice, and looked up, which was the first time, and said she had no suspicion of that kind; that my offer was so civil that she was as much ashamed to refuse it as she should be ashamed to accept it, if she was where she was known; that she thought I was not quite a stranger to her, for she had seen me before; that she would accept my offer so far as to sit at table, because I desired it; but she could not promise me to eat, and that she hoped I would take the other as a constraint upon her, in return to so much kindness.

She startled me when she said she had seen me before; for I had not the least knowledge of her, nor did I remember so much as to have heard of her name; for I had asked her name of her maid; and indeed it made me almost repent my compliment, for it was many ways essential to me not to be known. However, I could not go back; and, besides, if I was known, it was essentially necessary to me to know who it was that knew me, and by what circumstances; so I went on with my compliment.

We came to the inn but just before it was dark. I offered to hand my widow out of the coach, and she could not decline it; but though her hoods were not then much over her face, yet, being dark, I could see little of her then. I waited on her then into the stairfoot, and led her up the inn-stairs to a dining-room which the master of the house offered to show us, as if for the whole company; but she declined going in there, and said she desired rather to go directly to her chamber, and turning to her maid, bade her speak to the innkeeper to show her to her lodging-room. So I waited on her to the door, and took my leave, telling her I would expect her at supper.

In order to treat her moderately well, and not extravagantly, for I had no thoughts of anything farther than civility, which was the effect of mere compassion for the unhappiness of the most truly disconsolate woman that I ever met with; I say, in order to treat her handsomely, but not extravagantly, I provided what the house afforded, which was a couple of partridges and a very good dish of stewed oysters. They brought us up afterwards a neat's tongue and a ham that was almost cut quite down, but we ate none of it; for the other was fully enough for us both, and the maid made her supper off the oysters we had left, which were enough.

I mention this because it should appear I did not treat her as a person I was making any court to, for I had nothing of that in my thoughts; but merely in pity to the poor woman, who I saw in a circumstance that was indeed very unhappy.

When I gave her maid notice that supper was ready, she fetched her mistress, coming in before her with a candle in her hand, and then it was that I saw her face, and being in her dishabille, she had no hood over her eyes or black upon her head, when I was truly surprised to see one of the most beautiful faces upon earth. I saluted her, and led her to the fireside, the table, though spread, being too far from the fire, the weather being cold.

She was now something sociable, though very grave, and sighed often on account of her circumstances. But she so handsomely governed her grief, yet so artfully made it mingle itself with all her discourse, that it added exceedingly to her behaviour, which was every way most exquisitely genteel. I had a great deal of discourse with her, and upon many subjects, and by degrees took her name, that is to say, from herself, as I had done before from her maid; also the place where she lived, viz., near Ratcliff, or rather Stepney, where I asked her leave to pay her a visit when she thought fit to admit company, which she seemed to intimate would not be a great while.

It is a subject too surfeiting to entertain people with the beauty of a person they will never see. Let it suffice to tell them she was the most beautiful creature of her sex that I ever saw before or since; and it cannot be wondered if I was charmed with her the very first moment I saw her face. Her behaviour was likewise a beauty in itself, and was so extraordinary that I cannot say I can describe it.

The next day she was much more free than she was the first night, and I had so much conversation as to enter into particulars of things on both sides; also she gave me leave to come and see her house, which, however, I did not do under a fortnight or thereabouts, because I did not know how far she would dispense with the ceremony which it was necessary to keep up at the beginning of the mourning.

However, I came as a man that had business with her, relating to the ship her husband was dead out of, and the first time I came was admitted; and, in short, the first time I came I made love to her. She received that proposal with disdain. I cannot indeed say she treated me with any disrespect, but she said she abhorred the offer, and would hear no more of it.

How I came to make such a proposal to her I scarce knew then, though it was very much my intention from the first.

In the meantime I inquired into her circumstances and her character, and heard nothing but what was very agreeable of them both ; and, above all, I found she had the report of the best-humoured lady and the best-bred of all that part of the town ; and now I thought I had found what I had so often wished for to make me happy and had twice miscarried in, and resolved not to miss her, if it was possible to obtain her.

It came indeed a little into my thoughts that I was a married man, and had a second wife alive, who, though she was false to me and a whore, yet I was not legally divorced from her, and that she was my wife for all that. But I soon got over that part ; for, first, as she was a whore, and the marquis had confessed it to me, I was divorced in law, and I had a power to put her away. But having had the misfortune of fighting a duel, and being obliged to quit the country, I could not claim the legal process which was my right, and therefore might conclude myself as much divorced as if it had been actually done, and so that scruple vanished.

I suffered now two months to run without pressing my widow any more, only I kept a strict watch to find if any one else pretended to her. At the end of two months I visited her again, when I found she received me with more freedom, and we had no more sighs and sobs about the last husband ; and though she would not let me press my former proposal so far as I thought I might have done, yet I found I had leave to come again, and it was the article of decency which she stood upon as much as anything ; that I was not disagreeable to her, and that my using her so handsomely upon the road had given me a great advantage in her favour.

I went on gradually with her, and gave her leave to stand off for two months more. But then I told her the matter of decency, which was but a ceremony, was not to stand in competition with the matter of affection; and, in short, I could not bear any longer delay, but that, if she thought fit, we might marry privately; and, to cut the story short, as I did my courtship, in about five months I got her in the mind, and we were privately married, and that with so very exact a concealment that her maid, that was so instrumental in it, yet had no knowledge of it for near a month more.

I was now, not only in my imagination, but in reality, the most happy creature in the world, as I was so infinitely satisfied with my wife, who was indeed the best-humoured woman in the world, a most accomplished, beautiful creature indeed, perfectly well-bred, and had not one ill quality about her; and this happiness continued without the least interruption for about six years.

But I, that was to be the most unhappy fellow alive in the article of matrimony, had at last a disappointment of the worst sort even here. I had three fine children by her, and in her time of lying-in with the last she got some cold, that she did not in a long time get off; and, in short, she grew very sickly. In being so continually ill and out of order, she very unhappily got a habit of drinking cordials and hot liquors. Drink, like the devil, when it gets hold of any one, though but a little, it goes on by little and little to their destruction. So in my wife, her stomach being weak and faint, she first took this cordial, then that, till, in short, she could not live without them, and from a drop to a sup, from a sup to a dram, from a dram to a glass, and so on to two, till at last she took, in short, to what we call drinking.

As I likened drink to the devil, in its gradual possession of the habits and person, so it is yet more like the devil in its encroachment on us, where it gets hold of our senses. In short, my beautiful, good-humoured, modest, well-bred wife grew a beast, a slave to strong liquor, and would be drunk at her own table—nay, in her own closet by herself, till, instead of a well-made, fine shape, she was as fat as a hostess; her fine face, bloated and blotched, had not so much as the ruins of the most beautiful person alive—nothing remained but a good eye; that indeed she held to the last. In short, she lost her beauty, her shape, her manners, and at last her virtue; and, giving herself up to drinking, killed herself in about a year and a half after she first began that cursed trade, in which time she twice was exposed in the most scandalous manner with a captain of a ship, who, like a villain, took the advantage of her being in drink and not knowing what she did. But it had this unhappy effect, that instead of her being ashamed and repenting of it when she came to herself, it hardened her in the crime, and she grew as void of modesty at last as of sobriety.

Oh, the power of intemperance! and how it encroaches on the best dispositions in the world; how it comes upon us gradually and insensibly; and what dismal effects it works upon our morals, changing the most virtuous, regular, well-instructed, and well-inclined tempers into worse than brutal! That was a good story, whether real or invented, of the devil tempting a young man to murder his father. No, he said; that was unnatural. "Why, then," says the devil, "go and lie with your mother." "No," says he; "that is abominable." "Well, then," says the devil, "if you will do nothing else to oblige me, go and get drunk." "Ay, ay," says the fellow, "I will do that." So he went and made himself drunk as a swine, and when he was drunk, he murdered his father and lay with his mother.

Never was a woman more virtuous, modest, chaste, sober; she never so much as desired to drink anything strong; it was with the greatest entreaty that I could prevail with her to drink a glass or two of wine, and rarely, if ever, above one or two at a time; even in company she had no inclination to it. Not an immodest word ever came out of her mouth, nor would she suffer it in any one else in her hearing without resentment and abhorrence. But upon that weakness and illness after her last lying-in, as above, the nurse pressed her, whenever she found herself faint and a sinking of her spirits, to take this cordial and that dram, to keep up her spirits, till it became necessary even to keep her alive, and gradually increased to a habit, so that it was no longer her physic but her food. Her appetite sunk and went quite away, and she ate little or nothing, but came at last to such a dreadful height that, as I have said, she would be drunk in her own dressing-room by eleven o'clock in the morning, and, in short, at last was never sober.

In this life of hellish excess, as I have said, she lost all that was before so valuable in her, and a villain, if it be proper to call a man who was really a gentleman by such a name, who was an intimate acquaintance, coming to pretend a visit to her, made her and her maid so drunk together that he lay with them both; with the mistress, the maid being in the room, and with the maid, the mistress being in the room; after which he, it seems, took the like liberty with them both as often as he thought fit, till the wench, being with child, discovered it for herself, and for her mistress too. Let any one judge what was my case now. I, that for six years thought myself the happiest man alive, was now the most miserable, distracted creature. As to my wife, I loved her so well, and was so sensible of the disaster of her drinking being the occasion of it all, that I could not resent it to such a degree as I had done in her predecessor; but I pitied her heartily. However, I put away all her servants, and almost locked her up; that is to say, I set new people over her, who would not suffer any one to come near her without my knowledge.

But what to do with the villain that had thus abused both her and me, that was the question that remained. To fight him upon equal terms, I thought, was a little hard; that after a man had treated me as he had done, he deserved no fair play for his life. So I resolved to wait for him in Stepney fields, and which way he often came home pretty late, and pistol him in the dark, and, if possible, to let him know what I killed him for before I did it. But when I came to consider of this, it shocked my temper too as well as principle, and I could not be a murderer, whatever else I could be, or whatever I was provoked to be.

However, I resolved, on the other hand, that I would severely correct him for what he had done, and it was not long before I had an opportunity; for, hearing one morning that he was walking across the fields from Stepney to Shadwell, which way I knew he often went, I waited for his coming home again, and fairly met him.

I had not many words with him, but told him I had long looked for him; that he knew the villainy he had been guilty of in my family, and he could not believe, since he knew also that I was fully informed of it, but that I must be a great coward, as well as a cuckold, or that I would resent it, and that it was now a very proper time to call him to an account for it; and therefore bade him, if he durst show his face to what he had done, and defend the name of a captain of a man-of-war, as they said he had been, to draw.

He seemed surprised at the thing, and began to parley, and would lessen the crime of it; but I told him it was not a time to talk that way, since he could not deny the fact; and to lessen the crime was to lay it the more upon the woman, who, I was sure, if he had not first debauched with wine, he could never have brought to the rest; and, seeing he refused to draw, I knocked him down with my cane at one blow, and I would not strike him again while he lay on the ground, but waited to see him recover a little; for I saw plainly he was not killed. In a few minutes he came to himself again, and then I took him fast by one wrist, and caned him as severely as I was able, and as long as I could hold it for want of breath, but forbore his head, because I was resolved he should feel it. In this condition at last he begged for mercy, but I was deaf to all pity a great while, till he roared out like a boy soundly whipped. Then I took his sword from him and broke it before his face, and left him on the ground, giving him two or three kicks on the backside, and bade him go and take the law of me if he thought fit.

I had now as much satisfaction as indeed could be taken of a coward, and had no more to say to him; but as I knew it would make a great noise about the town, I immediately removed my family, and, that I might be perfectly concealed, went into the north of England, and lived in a little town called ——, not far from Lancaster, where I lived retired, and was no more heard of for about two years. My wife, though more confined than she used to be, and so kept up from the lewd part which, I believe, in the intervals of her intemperance, she was truly ashamed of and abhorred, yet retained the drinking part, which becoming, as I have said, necessary for her subsistence, she soon ruined her health, and in about a year and a half after my removal into the north she died.

Thus I was once more a free man, and, as one would think, should by this time have been fully satisfied that matrimony was not appointed to be a state of felicity to me.

I should have mentioned that the villain of a captain who I had drubbed, as above, pretended to make a great stir about my assaulting him on the highway, and that I had fallen upon him with three ruffians, with an intent to murder him ; and this began to obtain belief among the people in the neighbourhood. I sent him word of so much of it as I had heard, and told him I hoped it did not come from his own mouth ; but if it did, I expected he would publicly disown it, he himself declaring he knew it to be false, or else I should be forced to act the same thing over again, till I had disciplined him into better manners ; and that he might be assured that if he continued to pretend that I had anybody with me when I caned him, I would publish the whole story in print, and, besides that, would cane him again wherever I met him, and as often as I met him, till he thought fit to defend himself with his sword like a gentleman.

He gave me no answer to this letter ; and the satisfaction I had for that was, that I gave twenty or thirty copies of it about among the neighbours, which made it as public as if I had printed it (that is, as to his acquaintance and mine), and made him so hissed at and hated that he was obliged to remove into some other part of the town—whither I did not inquire.

My wife being now dead, I knew not what course to take in the world, and I grew so disconsolate and discouraged that I was next door to being distempered, and sometimes, indeed, I thought myself a little touched in my head. But it proved nothing but vapours and the vexation of this affair, and in about a year's time, or thereabouts, it wore off again.

I had rambled up and down in a most discontented, unsettled posture after this, I say, about a year, and then I considered I had three innocent children, and I could take no care of them, and that I must either go away and leave them to the wide world or settle here and get somebody to look after them, and that better a mother-in-law than no mother; for to live such a wandering life it would not do; so I resolved I would marry as anything offered, though it was mean, and the meaner the better. I concluded my next wife should be only taken as an upper servant; that is to say, a nurse to my children and housekeeper to myself; "and let her be whore or honest woman," said I, "as she likes best; I am resolved I will not much concern myself about that;" for I was now one desperate, that valued not how things went.

In this careless, and indeed rash, foolish humour, I talked to myself thus: "If I marry an honest woman, my children will be taken care of; if she be a slut and abuses me, as I see everybody does, I will kidnap her and send her to Virginia, to my plantations there, and there she shall work hard enough and fare hard enough to keep her chaste, I'll warrant her."

I knew well enough at first that these were mad, hare-brained notions, and I thought no more of being serious in them than I thought of being a man in the moon; but I know not how it happened to me, I reasoned and talked to myself in this wild manner so long that I brought myself to be seriously desperate; that is, to resolve upon another marriage, with all the suppositions of unhappiness that could be imagined to fall out.

And yet even this rash resolution of my senses did not come presently to action; for I was half a year after this before I fixed upon anything. At last, as he that seeks mischief shall certainly find it, so it was with me. There happened to be a young, or rather a middle-aged, woman in the next town, which was but a half-mile off, who usually was at my house and among my children every day when the weather was tolerable ; and though she came but merely as a neighbour, and to see us, yet she was always helpful in directing and ordering things for them, and mighty handy about them, as well before my wife died as after.

Her father was one that I employed often to go to Liverpool, and sometimes to Whitehaven, and do business for me ; for having, as it were, settled myself in the northern parts of England, I had ordered part of my effects to be shipped, as occasion of shipping offered, to either of those two towns, to which, the war continuing very sharp, it was safer coming, as to privateers, than about through the Channel to London.

I took a mighty fancy at last that this girl would answer my end, particularly that I saw she was mighty useful among the children ; so, on the other hand, the children loved her very well, and I resolved to love her too, flattering myself mightily, that as I had married two gentlewomen and one citizen, and they proved all three whores, I should now find what I wanted in an innocent country wench.

I took up a world of time in considering of this matter ; indeed scarce any of my matches were done without very mature consideration. The second was the worst in that article, but in this I thought of it, I believe, four months most seriously before I resolved, and that very prudence spoiled the whole thing. However, at last being resolved, I took Mrs Margaret one day as she passed by my parlour-door, called her in, and told her I wanted to speak with her. She came readily in, but blushed mightily when I bade her sit down in a chair just by me.

I used no great ceremony with her, but told her

that I had observed she had been mighty kind to my children, and was very tender to them, and that they all loved her, and that, if she and I could agree about it, I intended to make her their mother, if she was not engaged to somebody else. The girl sat still and said never a word till I said those words, "if she was not engaged to somebody else;" when she seemed struck. However, I took no notice of it, other than this, "Look ye, Moggy," said I (so they call them in the country), "if you have promised yourself, you must tell me." For we all knew that a young fellow, a good clergyman's wicked son, had hung about her a great while, two or three years, and made love to her, but could never get the girl in the mind, it seems, to have him.

She knew I was not ignorant of it, and therefore, after her first surprise was over, she told me Mr ⸺ had, as I knew, often come after her, but she had never promised him anything, and had for several years refused him; her father always telling her that he was a wicked fellow, and that he would be her ruin if she had him.

"Well, Moggy, then," says I, "what dost say to me? Art thou free to make me a wife?" She blushed and looked down upon the ground, and would not speak a good while; but when I pressed her to tell me, she looked up, and said she supposed I was but jesting with her. Well, I got over that, and told her I was in very good earnest with her, and I took her for a sober, honest, modest girl, and, as I said, one that my children loved mighty well, and I was in earnest with her; if she would give me her consent, I would give her my word that I would have her, and we would be married to-morrow morning. She looked up again at that, and smiled a little, and said no, that was too soon too to say yes. She hoped I would give her some time to consider of it, and to talk with her father about it.

I told her she needed not much time to consider about it; but, however, I would give her till to-morrow morning, which was a great while. By this time I had kissed Moggy two or three times, and she began to be freer with me; and when I pressed her to marry me the next morning, she laughed, and told me it was not lucky to be married in her old clothes.

I stopped her mouth presently with that, and told her she should not be married in her old clothes, for I would give her some new. "Ay, it may be afterwards," says Moggy, and laughed again. "No, just now," says I. "Come along with me, Moggy;" so I carried her upstairs into my wife's room that was, and showed her a new morning-gown of my wife's, that she had never worn above two or three times, and several other fine things. "Look you there, Moggy," says I, "there is a wedding-gown for you; give me your hand now that you will have me to-morrow morning. And as to your father, you know he has gone to Liverpool on my business, but I will answer for it he shall not be angry when he comes home to call his master son-in-law; and I ask him no portion. Therefore give me thy hand for it, Moggy," says I very merrily to her, and kissed her again; and the girl gave me her hand, and very pleasantly too, and I was mightily pleased with it, I assure you.

There lived about three doors from us an ancient gentleman who passed for a doctor of physic, but who was really a Romish priest in orders, as there are many in that part of the country; and in the evening I sent to speak with him. He knew that I understood his profession, and that I had lived in popish countries, and, in a word, believed me a Roman too, for I was such abroad. When he came to me I told him

"I pressed her to marry me the next morning"

the occasion for which I sent for him, and that it was to be to-morrow morning. He readily told me, if I would come and see him in the evening, and bring Moggy with me, he would marry us in his own study, and that it was rather more private to do it in the evening than in the morning. So I called Moggy again to me, and told her, since she and I had agreed the matter for to-morrow, it was as well to be done over-night, and told her what the doctor had said.

Moggy blushed again, and said she must go home first, that she could not be ready before to-morrow. "Look ye, Moggy," says I, "you are my wife now, and you shall never go away from me a maid. I know what you mean; you would go home to shift you. Come, Moggy," says I, "come along with me again upstairs." So I carried her to a chest of linen, where were several new shifts of my last wife's, which she had never worn at all, and some that had been worn.

"There is a clean smock for you, Moggy," says I, "and to-morrow you shall have all the rest." When I had done this, "Now, Moggy," says I, "go and dress you;" so I locked her in, and went downstairs. "Knock," says I, "when you are dressed."

After some time Moggy did not knock, but down she came into my room, completely dressed, for there were several other things that I bade her take, and the clothes fitted her as if they had been made for her. It seems she slipped the lock back.

"Well, Moggy," says I, "now you see you shan't be married in your old clothes;" so I took her in my arms and kissed her; and well pleased I was as ever I was in my life, or with anything I ever did in my life. As soon as it was dark Moggy slipped away before-hand, as the doctor and I had agreed, to the old gentleman's housekeeper, and I came in about half-an-hour after; and there we were married in the doctor's study

—that is to say, in his oratory or chapel, a little room within his study—and we stayed and supped with him afterwards.

Then, after a short stay more, I went home first, because I would send the children all to bed, and the other servants out of the way; and Moggy came some time after, and so we lay together that night. The next morning I let all the family know that Moggy was my wife, and my three children were rejoiced at it to the last degree. And now I was a married man a fourth time; and, in short, I was really more happy in this plain country girl than with any of all the wives I had had. She was not young, being about thirty-three, but she brought me a son the first year. She was very pretty, well-shaped, and of a merry, cheerful disposition, but not a beauty. She was an admirable family manager, loved my former children, and used them not at all the worse for having some of her own. In a word, she made me an excellent wife, but lived with me but four years, and died of a hurt she got of a fall while she was with child, and in her I had a very great loss indeed.

And yet such was my fate in wives, that, after all the blushing and backwardness of Mrs Moggy at first, Mrs Moggy had, it seems, made a slip in her younger days, and was got with child ten years before, by a gentleman of a great estate in that country, who promised her marriage, and afterwards deserted her. But as that had happened long before I came into the country, and the child was dead and forgotten, the people were so good to her, and so kind to me, that, hearing I had married her, nobody ever spoke of it; neither did I ever hear of it or suspect it till after she was in her grave, and then it was of small consequence to me one way or other; and she was a faithful, virtuous, obliging wife to me. I had very severe affliction indeed while she lived with me; for the smallpox, a frightful distemper in that country, broke into my family, and carried off three of my children and a maid-servant; so that I had only one of my former wife's, and one by my Moggy, the first a son, the last a daughter.

While these things were in agitation came on the invasion of the Scots and the fight at Preston; and I have cause to bless the memory of my Moggy; for I was all on fire on that side, and just going away with horse and arms to join the Lord Derwentwater. But Moggy begged me off (as I may call it), and hung about me so with her tears and importunities that I sat still and looked on; for which I had reason to be thankful.

I was really a sorrowful father, and the loss of my children stuck close to me; but the loss of my wife stuck closer to me than all the rest. Nor was my grief lessened or my kindest thoughts abated in the least by the account I heard of her former miscarriages, seeing they were so long before I knew her, and were not discovered by me or to me in her lifetime.

All these things put together made me very comfortless. And now I thought Heaven summoned me to retire to Virginia, the place, and, as I may say, the only place, I had been blessed at, or had met with anything that deserved the name of success in, and where, indeed, my affairs being in good hands, the plantations were increased to such a degree that some years my return here made up eight hundred pounds, and one year almost a thousand. So I resolved to leave my native country once more, and taking my son with me, and leaving Moggy's daughter with her grandfather, I made him my principal agent, left him considerable in his hands for the maintenance of the child, and left my will in his hand, by which, if I died before I should otherwise provide for her, I left her £2000 portion, to be paid by my son out of the estate I had in Virginia, and the whole estate, if he died unmarried.

I embarked for Virginia in the year ———, at the town of Liverpool, and had a tolerable voyage thither, only that we met with a pirate ship, in the latitude of 48 degrees, who plundered us of everything they could come at that was for their turn; that is to say, provisions, ammunition, small-arms, and money. But, to give the rogues their due, though they were the most abandoned wretches that were ever seen, they did not use us ill. And as to my loss, it was not considerable; the cargo which I had on board was in goods, and was of no use to them; nor could they come at those things without rummaging the whole ship, which they did not think worth their while.

I found all my affairs in very good order at Virginia, my plantations prodigiously increased, and my manager, who first inspired me with travelling thoughts, and made me master of any knowledge worth naming, received me with a transport of joy, after a ramble of four-and-twenty years.

I ought to remember it, to the encouragement of all faithful servants, that he gave me an account, which, I believe, was critically just, of the whole affairs of the plantations, each by themselves, and balanced in years, every year's produce being fully transmitted, charges deducted, to my order at London.

I was exceedingly satisfied, as I had good reason indeed, with his management; and with his management, as much in its degree, of his own I can safely say it. He had improved a very large plantation of his own at the same time, which he began upon the foot of the country's allowance of land and the encouragement he had from me.

When he had given me all this pleasing, agreeable

account, you will not think it strange that I had a
desire to see the plantations, and to view all the
servants, which, in both the works, were upwards of
three hundred; and as my tutor generally bought
some every fleet that came from England, I had the
mortification to see two or three of the Preston gentlemen there, who, being prisoners of war, were spared
from the public execution, and sent over to that slavery,
which to gentlemen must be worse than death.

I do not mention what I did or said relating to
them here. I shall speak at large of it when the rest
of them came over, which more nearly concerned me.

But one circumstance occurred to me here that
equally surprised me and terrified me to the last
degree. Looking over all the servants, as I say above,
and viewing the plantations narrowly and frequently,
I came one day by a place where some women were at
work by themselves. I was seriously reflecting on the
misery of human life, when I saw some of those poor
wretches. Thought I, "They have perhaps lived gay
and pleasantly in the world, notwithstanding, through
a variety of distresses, they may have been brought to
this; and if a body was to hear the history of some
of them now, it would perhaps be as moving and as
seasonable a sermon as any minister in the country
could preach."

While I was musing thus and looking at the women,
on a sudden I heard a combustion among other of the
women-servants, who were almost behind me, in the
same work, and help was called loudly for, one of the
women having swooned away. They said she would
die immediately if something was not done to relieve
her. I had nothing about me but a little bottle, which
we always carried about us there with rum, to give any
servant a dram that merited that favour; so I turned
my horse and went up towards the place. But as

the poor creature was lying flat on the ground, and the rest of the women-servants about her, I did not see her, but gave them the bottle, and they rubbed her temples with it, and, with much ado, brought her to life, and gave her a little to drink. But she could drink none of it, and was exceeding ill afterwards, so that she was carried to the infirmary—so they call it in the religious houses in Italy where the sick nuns and friars are carried; but here, in Virginia, I think they should call it the condemned hole, for it really was only a place just fit for people to die in, not a place to be cured in.

The sick woman refusing to drink, one of the women-servants brought me the bottle again, and I bade them drink it among them, which had almost set them together by the ears for the liquor, there being not enough to give every one a sup.

I went home to my house immediately, and reflecting on the miserable provision was wont to be made for poor servants when they were sick, I inquired of my manager if it was so still. He said he believed mine was better than any in the country; but he confessed it was but sad lodging. However, he said he would go and look after it immediately and see how it was.

He came to me again about an hour after, and told me the woman was very ill, and frighted with her condition; that she seemed to be very penitent for some things in her past life, which lay heavy upon her mind, believing she should die; that she asked him if there was no minister to comfort poor dying servants; and he told her that she knew they had no minister nearer than such a place, but that, if she lived till morning, he should be sent for. He told me, also, that he had removed her into a room where their chief workman used to lodge; that he had given her a pair of sheets, and everything he could that he thought she wanted, and had appointed another woman-servant to tend her and sit up with her.

"Well," says I, "that's well; for I cannot bear to have poor creatures lie and perish, by the mere hardship of the place they are in, when they are sick and want help. Besides," said I, "some of those unfortunate creatures they call convicts may be people that have been tenderly brought up." "Really, sir," says he, "this poor creature, I always said, had something of a gentlewoman in her. I could see it by her behaviour, and I have heard the other women say that she lived very great once, and that she had fifteen hundred pound to her portion; and I dare say she has been a handsome woman in her time, and she has a hand as fine as a lady's now, though it be tanned with the weather. I dare say she was never brought up to labour as she does here, and she says to the rest that it will kill her."

"Truly," says I, "it may be so, and that may be the reason that she faints under it;" and I added, "Is there nothing you can put her to within doors that may not be so laborious and expose her to so much heat and cold?" He told me yes, there was. He could set her to be the housekeeper, for the woman that lately was such was out of her time, and was married and turned planter. "Why, then, let her have it," said I, "if she recovers; and in the meantime go," said I, "and tell her so; perhaps the comfort of it may help to restore her."

He did so, and with that, taking good care of her, and giving her good warm diet, the woman recovered, and in a little time was abroad again; for it was the mere weight of labour, and being exposed to hard lodging and mean diet, to one so tenderly bred, that struck her and she fainted at her work.

When she was made housekeeper she was quite another body. She put all the household into such excellent order, and managed their provisions so well, that my tutor admired her conduct, and would be every now and then speaking of her to me, that she was an excellent manager. " I'll warrant," says he, " she has been bred a gentlewoman, and she has been a fine woman in her time too." In a word, he said so many good things of her that I had a mind to see her. So one day I took occasion to go to the plantation-house, as they called it, and into a parlour always reserved for the master of the plantation. There she had opportunity to see me before I could see her, and as soon as she had seen me she knew me; but indeed had I seen her an hundred times I should not have known her. She was, it seems, in the greatest confusion and surprise at seeing who I was that it was possible for any one to be; and when I ordered my manager to bring her into the room, he found her crying, and begged him to excuse her, that she was frighted, and should die away if she came near me.

I, not imagining anything but that the poor creature was afraid of me (for masters in Virginia are terrible things), bade him tell her she need to be under no concern at my calling for her; for it was not for any hurt nor for any displeasure, but that I had some orders to give her. So, having, as he thought, encouraged her, though her surprise was of another kind, he brought her in. When she came in she held a handkerchief in her hand, wiping her eyes, as if she had cried. "Mrs Housekeeper," said I, speaking cheerfully to her, " don't be concerned at my sending for you; I have had a very good account of your management, and I called for you to let you know I am very well pleased with it; and if it falls in my way to do you any good, if your circumstances

*"I am your miserable divorced wife."*

will allow it, I may be willing enough to help you out of your misery."

She made low courtesies, but said nothing. However, she was so far encouraged that she took her hand from her face, and I saw her face fully; and I believe she did it desiring I should discover who she was; but I really knew nothing of her, any more than if I had never seen her in my life, but went on, as I thought, to encourage her, as I used to do with any that I saw deserved it.

In the meantime my tutor, who was in the room, went out on some business or other—I know not what. As soon as he was gone she burst out into a passion, and fell down on her knees just before me: "Oh, sir!" says she, "I see you don't know me. Be merciful to me; I am your miserable divorced wife!"

I was astonished; I was frighted; I trembled like one in an ague; I was speechless; in a word, I was ready to sink, and she fell flat on her face, and lay there as if she had been dead. I was speechless, I say, as a stone. I had only presence of mind enough to step to the door and fasten it, that my tutor might not come in; then, going back to her, I took her up and spoke comfortably to her, and told her I no more knew her than if I had never seen her.

"Oh, sir!" said she, "afflictions are dreadful things; such as I have suffered have been enough to alter my countenance; but forgive," said she, "for God's sake, the injuries I have done you. I have paid dear for all my wickedness, and it is just, it is righteous, that God should bring me to your foot, to ask your pardon for all my brutish doings. Forgive me, sir," said she, "I beseech you, and let me be your slave or servant for it as long as I live; it is all I ask;" and with those words she fell upon her knees again and cried so vehemently that it was impossible for her to stop it

II.                                                                G or to speak a word more. I took her up again, made her sit down, desired her to compose herself, and to hear what I was going to say; though indeed it touched me so sensibly that I was hardly able to speak any more than she was.

First, I told her it was such a surprise to me that I was not able to say much to her; and indeed the tears run down my face almost as fast as they did on hers. I told her that I should only tell her now, that, as nobody had yet known anything that had passed, so it was absolutely necessary not a word of it should be known; that it should not be the worse for her that she was thus thrown in my hands again; but that I could do nothing for her if it was known, and, therefore, that her future good or ill fortune would depend upon her entire concealing it; that, as my manager would come in again presently, she should go back to her part of the house, and go on in the business as she did before; that I would come to her and talk more at large with her in a day or two. So she retired, after assuring me that not a word of it should go out of her mouth; and indeed she was willing to retire before my tutor came again, that he might not see the agony she was in.

I was so perplexed about this surprising incident that I hardly knew what I did or said all that night; nor was I come to any settled resolution in the morning what course to take in it. However, in the morning I called my tutor, and told him that I had been exceedingly concerned about the poor distressed creature, the housekeeper; that I had heard some of her story, which was very dismal; that she had been in very good circumstances and was bred very well, and that I was glad he had removed her out of the field into the house; but still she was almost naked, and that I would have him go down to the warehouse and give her some linen, especially head-clothes, and all sorts of small things such as hoods, gloves, stockings, shoes, petticoats, &c., and to let her choose for herself; also a morning-gown of calico, and a mantua of a better kind of calico; that is to say, new clothe her; which he did, but brought me word that he found her all in tears, and that she had cried all night long, and, in short, he believed she would indeed cry herself to death; that all the while she was receiving the things he gave her she cried; that now and then she would struggle with and stop it, but that then, upon another word speaking, she would burst out again, so that it grieved everybody that saw her.

I was really affected with her case very much, but struggled hard with myself to hide it, and turned the discourse to something else. In the meantime, though I did not go to her the next day, nor till the third day, yet I studied day and night how to act, and what I should do in this remarkable case.

When I came to the house, which was the third day, she came into the room I was in, clothed all over with my things which I had ordered her, and told me she thanked God she was now my servant again and wore my livery, thanked me for the clothes I had sent her, and said it was much more than she had deserved from me.

I then entered into discourses with her, nobody being present but ourselves; and first I told her she should name no more of the unkind things that had passed, for she had humbled herself more than enough on that subject, and I would never reproach her with anything that was past. I found that she had been the deepest sufferer by far. I told her it was impossible for me, in my present circumstances, to receive her there as a wife who came over as a convict, neither did she know so little as to desire it; but I told her I might be instrumental to put an end to her misfortunes in the world, and especially to the miserable part of it which was her present load, provided she could effectually keep her own counsel and never let the particulars come out of her mouth, and that from the day she did she might date her irrevocable ruin.

She was as sensible of the necessity of that part as I was, and told me all she could claim of me would be only to deliver her from her present calamity that she was not able to support; and that then, if I pleased, she might live such a life as that she might apply the residue of what time she should have wholly to repentance; that she was willing to do the meanest offices in the world for me; and though she should rejoice to hear that I would forgive her former life, yet that she would not look any higher than to be my servant as long as she lived; and, in the meantime, I might be satisfied she would never let any creature so much as know that I had ever seen her before.

I asked her if she was willing to let me into any part of the history of her life since she and I parted; but I did not insist upon it otherwise than as she thought convenient. She said, as her breach with me began first in folly and ended in sin, so her whole life afterwards was a continued series of calamity, sin and sorrow, sin and shame, and at last misery; that she was deluded into gay company and to an expensive way of living which betrayed her to several wicked courses to support the expenses of it; that after a thousand distresses and difficulties, being not able to maintain herself, she was reduced to extreme poverty; that she would many times have humbled herself to me in the lowest and most submissive manner in the world, being sincerely penitent for her first crime, but that she could never hear of me, nor which way I was gone; that she was by that means so abandoned that she wanted bread, and those wants and distresses brought her into bad company of another kind, and that she fell in among a gang of thieves, with whom she herded for some time, and got money enough a great while, but under the greatest dread and terror imaginable, being in the constant fear of coming to shame ; that afterwards what she feared was come upon her, and for a very trifling attempt in which she was not principal, but accidentally concerned, she was sent to this place. She told me her life was such a collection of various fortunes—up and down, in plenty and in misery, in prison and at liberty, at ease and in torment—that it would take up a great many days to give me a history of it ; that I was come to see the end of it, as I had seen the best part of the beginning ; that I knew she was brought up tenderly and fared delicately ; but that now she was, with the prodigal, brought to desire husks with swine, and even to want that supply. Her tears flowed so strongly upon this discourse that they frequently interrupted her, so that she could not go on without difficulty, and at last could not go on at all. So I told her I would excuse her telling any more of her story at that time ; that I saw it was but a renewing of her grief, and that I would rather contribute to her forgetting what was past, and desired her to say no more of it ; so I broke off that part.

In the meantime I told her, since Providence had thus cast her upon my hands again, I would take care that she should not want, and that she should not live hardly neither, though I could go no further at present ; and thus we parted for that time, and she continued in the business of housekeeper ; only that, to ease her, I gave her an assistant ; and, though I would not have it called so, it was neither more or less than a servant to wait on her and do everything for her ; and told her, too, that it was so.

After she had been some time in this place she recovered her spirits and grew cheerful; her fallen flesh plumped up, and the sunk and hollow parts filled again, so that she began to recover something of that brightness and charming countenance which was once so very agreeable to me; and sometimes I could not help having warm desires towards her, and of taking her into her first station again; but there were many difficulties occurred which I could not get over a great while.

But in the meantime another odd accident happened which put me to a very great difficulty, and more than I could have thought such a thing could be capable of. My tutor, a man of wit and learning, and full of generous principles, who was at first moved with compassion for the misery of this gentlewoman, and, even then, thought there were some things more than common in her, as I have hinted; now when, as I say, she was recovered, and her sprightly temper restored and comforted, he was charmed so with her conversation that, in short, he fell in love with her.

I hinted in my former account of her that she had a charming tongue, was mistress of abundance of wit, that she sung incomparably fine, and was perfectly well-bred. These all remained with her still, and made her a very agreeable person; and, in short, he came to me one evening and told me that he came to ask my leave to let him marry the housekeeper.

I was exceedingly perplexed at this proposal, but, however, I gave him no room to perceive that. I told him I hoped he had considered well of it before he brought it so far as to offer it to me, and supposed that he had agreed that point so that I had no consent to give, but as she had almost four years of her time to serve.

He answered no; he paid such a regard to me that

he would not so much as take one step in such a thing without my knowledge, and assured me he had not so much as mentioned it to her. I knew not what answer indeed to make to him, but at last I resolved to put it off from myself to her, because then I should have opportunity to talk with her beforehand. So I told him he was perfectly free to act in the matter as he thought fit; that I could not say either one thing or another to it, neither had I any right to meddle in it. As to her serving out her time with me, that was a trifle, and not worth naming, but I hoped he would consider well every circumstance before he entered upon such an affair as that.

He told me he had fully considered it already, and that he was resolved, seeing I was not against it, to have her whatever came of it, for he believed he should be the happiest man alive with her. Then he ran on in his character of her, how clever a woman she was in the management of all manner of business, how admirable conversation she was, what a wit, what a memory, what a vast share of knowledge, and the like; all which I knew to be the truth, and yet short of her just character too; for, as she was all that formerly when she was mine, she was vastly improved in the school of affliction, and was all the bright part, with a vast addition of temper, prudence, judgment, and all that she formerly wanted.

I had not much patience, as you may well imagine, till I saw my honest housekeeper, to communicate this secret to her, and to see what course she would steer on so nice an occasion. But I was suddenly taken so ill with a cold which held for two days that I could not stir out of doors; and in this time the matter was all done and over; for my tutor had gone the same night and made his attack; but was coldly received at first, which very much surprised him, for he made no doubt to have her consent at first word. However, the next day he came again, and again the third day, when, finding he was in earnest, and yet that she could not think of anything of that kind, she told him, in few words, that she thought herself greatly obliged to him for such a testimony of his respect to her, and should have embraced it willingly, as anybody would suppose one in her circumstances should do, but that she would not abuse him so much, for that she must acknowledge to him she was under obligations that prevented her; that was, in short, that she was a married woman and had a husband alive.

This was so sincere but so effectual an answer that he could have no room to reply one word to it, but that he was very sorry, and that it was a very great affliction to him, and as great a disappointment as ever he met with.

The next day after he had received this repulse I came to the plantation-house, and, sending for the housekeeper, I began with her, and told her that I understood she would have a very advantageous proposal made to her, and that I would have her consider well of it, and then told her what my tutor had said to me.

She immediately fell a-crying, at which I seemed to wonder very much. "Oh, sir!" says she, "how can you name such a thing to me?" I told her that I could name it the better to her because I had been married myself since I parted from her. "Yes, sir," says she; "but the case alters; the crime being on my side, I ought not to marry; but," says she, "that is not the reason at all, but I cannot do it." I pretended to press her to it, though not sincerely, I must acknowledge, for my heart had turned toward her for some time, and I had fully forgiven her in my mind all her former conduct; but, I say, I seemed to press her to it, at which she burst out in a passion. "No, no," says she; "let me be your slave rather than the best man's wife in the world." I reasoned with her upon her circumstances, and how such a marriage would restore her to a state of ease and plenty, and none in the world might ever know or suspect who or what she had been. But she could not bear it; but, with tears, again raising her voice that I was afraid she would be heard, "I beseech you," says she, "do not speak of it any more. I was once yours, and I will never belong to any man else in the world. Let me be as I am, or anything else you please to make me, but not a wife to any man alive but yourself."

I was so moved with the passion she was in at speaking this that I knew not what I said or did for some time. At length I said to her, "It is a great pity you had not long ago been as sincere as you are now; it had been better for us both. However, as it is, you shall not be forced to anything against your mind, nor shall you be the worse treated for refusing; but how will you put him off? No doubt he expects you will receive his proposal as an advantage; and as he sees no farther into your circumstances, so it is." "Oh, sir!" says she, "I have done all that already. He has his answer, and is fully satisfied. He will never trouble you any more on that head;" and then she told me what answer she had given him.

From that minute I resolved that I would certainly take her again to be my wife as before. I thought she had fully made me amends for her former ill conduct, and she deserved to be forgiven (and so indeed she did, if ever woman did, considering also what dreadful penance she had undergone, and how long she had lived in misery and distress); and that Providence had, as it were, cast her upon me again, and, above all, had given her such an affection to me and so resolved a mind that she could refuse so handsome an offer of deliverance rather than be farther separated from me.

As I resolved this in my mind, so I thought it was cruel to conceal it any longer from her. Nor, indeed, could I contain myself any longer, but I took her in my arms: "Well," says I, "you have given me such a testimony of affection in this that I can no longer withstand. I forgive you all that ever was between us on this account, and, since you will be nobody's but mine, you shall be mine again as you were at first."

But this was too much for her the other way, and now she was so far overcome with my yielding to her that, had she not got vent to her passion by the most vehement crying, she must have died in my arms; and I was forced to let her go and set her down in a chair, where she cried for a quarter of an hour before she could speak a word.

When she was come to herself enough to talk again, I told her we must consider of a method how to bring this to pass, and that it must not be done by publishing there that she was my wife before, for that would expose us both, but that I would openly marry her again. This she agreed was very rational, and accordingly, about two months after, we were married again, and no man in the world ever enjoyed a better wife or lived more happy than we both did for several years after.

And now I began to think my fortunes were settled for this world, and I had nothing before me but to finish a life of infinite variety, such as mine had been, with a comfortable retreat, being both made wiser by our sufferings and difficulties, and able to judge for ourselves what kind of life would be best adapted to our present circumstances, and in what station we might look upon ourselves to be most completely happy.

But man is a short-sighted creature at best, and in nothing more than in that of fixing his own felicity, or, as we may say, choosing for himself. One would have thought, and so my wife often suggested to me, that the state of life that I was now in was as perfectly calculated to make a man completely happy as any private station in the world could be. We had an estate more than sufficient, and daily increasing, for the supporting any state or figure that in that place we could propose to ourselves or even desire to live in ; we had everything that was pleasant and agreeable, without the least mortification in any circumstances of it ; every sweet thing, and nothing to embitter it ; every good, and no mixture of evil with it ; nor any gap open where we could have the least apprehensions of any evil breaking out upon us. Nor indeed was it easy for either of us, in our phlegmatic, melancholy notions, to have the least imagination how anything disastrous could happen to us in the common course of things, unless something should befall us out of the ordinary way of Providence, or of its acting in the world.

But an unseen mine blew up all this apparent tranquillity at once ; and though it did not remove my affairs there from me, yet it effectually removed me from them and sent me a-wandering into the world again—a condition full of hazards, and always attended with circumstances dangerous to mankind, while he is left to choose his own fortunes and be guided by his own short-sighted measures.

I must now return to a circumstance of my history which had been past for some time, and which relates to my conduct while I was last in England.

I mentioned how my faithful wife Moggy, with her tears and her entreaties, had prevailed with me not to play the madman and openly join in the rebellion with the late Lord Derwentwater and his party when they entered Lancashire, and thereby, as I may say, saved my life. But my curiosity prevailed so much at last that I gave her the slip when they came to Preston, and at least thought I would go and look at them, and see what they were likely to come to.

My former wife's importunities, as above, had indeed prevailed upon me from publicly embarking in that enterprise and joining openly with them in arms; and by this, as I have observed, she saved my life to be sure, because I had then publicly espoused the rebellion, and had been known to have been among them, which might have been as fatal to me afterwards, though I had not been taken in the action, as if I had.

But when they advanced and came nearer to us to Preston, and there appeared a greater spirit among the people in their favour, my old doctor, whom I mentioned before, who was a Romish priest, and had married us, inspired me with new zeal, and gave me no rest till he obliged me, with only a good horse and arms, to join them the day before they entered Preston, he himself venturing in the same posture with me.

I was not so public here as to be very well known, at least by any one that had knowledge of me in the country where I lived; and this was indeed my safety afterwards, as you will soon hear. But yet I was known too among the men, especially among the Scots, with some of whom I had been acquainted in foreign service. With these I was particularly conversant, and, passing for a French officer, I talked to them of making a select detachment to defend the pass between Preston and the river and bridge, upon maintaining which, as I insisted, depended the safety of the whole party.

It was with some warmth that I spoke of that

affair, and as I passed among them, I say, for a French officer and a man of experience, it caused several debates among them. But the hint was not followed, as is well known, and from that moment I gave them all up as lost, and meditated nothing but how to escape from them, which I effected the night before they were surrounded by the royal cavalry. I did not do this without great difficulty, swimming the river Ribble at a place where, though I got well over, yet I could not for a long while get to a place where my horse could land himself—that is to say, where the ground was firm enough for him to take the land. However, at length I got on shore, and riding very hard, came the next evening in sight of my own dwelling. Here, after lying by in a wood till the depth of night, I shot my horse in a little kind of a gravel pit, or marl pit, where I soon covered him with earth for the present, and marching all alone, I came about two in the morning to my house, where my wife, surprised with joy and yet terribly frighted, let me in ; and then I took immediate measures to secure myself upon whatever incident might happen, but which, as things were ordered, I had no need to make use of, for the rebels being entirely defeated, and either all killed or taken prisoners, I was not known by anybody in the country to have been among them ; no, nor so much as suspected. And thus I made a narrow escape from the most dangerous action, and most foolishly embarked in, of any that I had ever been engaged in before.

It was very lucky to me that I killed and buried my horse, for he would have been taken two days after, and would, to be sure, have been known by those who had seen me upon him at Preston. But now, as none knew I had been abroad, nor any such circumstance could discover me, I kept close, and as my excursion had been short and I had not been missed by any of my neighbours, if anybody came to speak with me, behold I was at home.

However, I was not thoroughly easy in my mind, and secretly wished I was in my own dominions in Virginia, to which, in a little time, other circumstances occurring, I made preparations to remove with my whole family.

In the meantime, as above, the action at Preston happened, and the miserable people surrendered to the king's troops. Some were executed for examples, as in such cases is usual, and the government extending mercy to the multitude, they were kept in Chester Castle and other places a considerable time, till they were disposed of, some one way, some another, as we shall hear.

Several hundreds of them after this were, at their own request, transported, as it is vulgarly expressed, to the plantations—that is to say, sent to Virginia and other British colonies to be sold after the usual manner of condemned criminals, or, as we call them there, convicts, to serve a limited time in the country, and then be made freemen again. Some of these I have spoken of above; but now, to my no little uneasiness, I found, after I had been there some time, two ships arrived with more of these people in the same river where all my plantations lay.

I no sooner heard of it but the first step I took was to resolve to let none of them be bought into my work or to any of my plantations; and this I did, pretending that I would not make slaves every day of unfortunate gentlemen who fell into that condition for their zeal to their party only, and the like. But the true reason was, that I expected several of them would know me, and might perhaps betray me, and make it public that I was one of the same sort, but had made my escape; and so I might be brought into trouble, and,

if I came off with my life, might have all my effects
seized on, and be reduced to misery and poverty again
at once, all which I thought I had done enough to
deserve.

This was a just caution, but, as I found quickly,
was not a sufficient one, as my circumstances stood,
for my safety ; for though I bought none of these poor
men myself, yet several of my neighbours did, and
there was scarce a plantation near me but had some
of them, more or less, among them ; so that, in a
word, I could not peep abroad hardly but I was in
danger to be seen, and known too, by some or other
of them.

I may be allowed to say that this was a very uneasy life to me, and such that, in short, I found
myself utterly unable to bear ; for I was now reduced
from a great man, a magistrate, a governor or master
of three great plantations, and having three or four
hundred servants at my command, to be a poor self-
condemned rebel, and durst not show my face ; and
that I might with the same safety, or rather more,
have skulked about in Lancashire where I was, or
gone up to London and concealed myself there till
things had been over.   But now the danger was come
home to me, even to my door, and I expected nothing
but to be informed against every day, be taken up, and
sent to England in irons, and have all my plantations
seized on as a forfeited estate to the Crown.

I had but one hope of safety to trust to, and that
was, that having been so little a while among them,
done nothing for them, and passing for a stranger, they
never knew my name, but only I was called the French
colonel, or the French officer, or the French gentleman by most, if not by all, the people here.   And as for
the doctor that went with me, he had found means to
escape too, though not the same way that I did, finding

the cause not likely to be supported, and that the king's troops were gathering on all sides round them like a cloud.

But to return to myself; this was no satisfaction to me, and what to do I really knew not, for I was more at a loss how to shift in such a distressed case as this, now it lay so close to me, than ever I was in any difficulty in my life. The first thing I did was to come home and make a confidence of the whole affair to my wife; and though I did it generously without conditions, yet I did not do it without first telling her how I was now going to put my life into her hands, that she might have it in her power to pay me home for all that she might think had been hard in my former usage of her; and that, in short, it would be in her power to deliver me up into the hands of my enemies, but that I would trust her generosity, as well as her renewed affection, and put all upon her fidelity, and without any more precaution I opened the whole thing to her, and particularly the danger I was now in.

A faithful counsellor is life from the dead, gives courage where the heart is sinking, and raises the mind to a proper use of means; and such she was to me indeed upon every step of this affair, and it was by her direction that I took every step that followed for the extricating myself out of this labyrinth.

"Come, come, my dear," says she, "if this be all, there is no room for any such disconsolate doings as your fears run you upon;" for I was immediately for selling off my plantations and all my stock and embarking myself forthwith, and to get to Madeira or to any place out of the king's dominions.

But my wife was quite of another opinion, and encouraging me on another account, proposed two things, either my freighting a sloop with provisions to

the West Indies, and so taking passage from thence to
London, or letting her go away directly for England
and endeavour to obtain the king's pardon, whatever it
might cost.

I inclined to the last proposal; for though I was
unhappily prejudiced in favour of a wrong interest, yet
I had always a secret and right notion of the clemency
and merciful disposition of his Majesty, and, had I been
in England, should, I believe, have been easily persuaded to have thrown myself at his foot.

But going to England as I was circumstanced must
have been a public action, and I must have made all
the usual preparations for it, must have appeared in
public, have stayed till the crop was ready, and gone
away in form and state as usual, or have acted as if
something extraordinary was the matter, and have filled
the heads of the people there with innumerable sugges-
tions of they knew not what.

But my wife made all this easy to me from her
own invention; for, without acquainting me of anything,
she comes merrily to me one morning before I was
up: "My dear," says she, "I am very sorry to hear
that you are not very well this morning. I have ordered
Pennico" (that was a young negro girl which I had
given her) "to make you a fire in your chamber, and
pray lie still where you are a while till it is done." At
the same instant the little negro came in with wood
and a pair of bellows, &c., to kindle the fire, and my
wife, not giving me time to reply, whispers close to my
ear to lie still and say nothing till she came up again
to me.

I was thoroughly frighted, that you may be sure of,
and thought of nothing but of being discovered, betrayed, and carried to England, hanged, quartered, and
all that was terrible, and my very heart sunk within
me. She perceived my disorder and turned back,

assuring me there was no harm, desired me to be easy, and she would come back again presently and give me satisfaction in every particular that I could desire. So I composed myself a while as well as I could, but it was but a little while that I could bear it, and I sent Pennico downstairs to find out her mistress, and tell her I was very ill and must speak with her immediately ; and the girl was scarce out of the room before I jumped out of bed and began to dress me, that I might be ready for all events.

My wife was as good as her word, and was coming up as the girl was coming down. "I see," says she, "you want patience, but pray do not want government of yourself, but take that screen before your face, and go to the window and see if you know any of those Scotchmen that are in the yard, for there are seven or eight of them come about some business to your clerk."

I went and looked through the screen, and saw the faces of them all distinctly, but could make nothing of them other than that they were Scotchmen, which was easy to discern. However, it was no satisfaction to me that I knew not their faces, for they might know mine for all that, according to the old English proverb, "That more knows Tom Fool than Tom Fool knows ;" so I kept close in my chamber till I understood they were all gone.

After this my wife caused it to be given out in the house that I was not well ; and when this not being well had lasted three or four days, I had my leg wrapped up in a great piece of flannel and laid upon a stool, and there I was lame of the gout ; and this served for about six weeks, when my wife told me she had given it out that my gout was rather rheumatic than a settled gout, and that I was resolved to take one of my own sloops and go away to Nevis or Antigua, and use the hot baths there for my cure.

All this was very well, and I approved my wife's contrivance as admirably good, both to keep me within doors eight or ten weeks at first, and to convey me away afterwards without any extraordinary bustle to be made about it; but still I did not know what it all tended to, and what the design of it all was. But my wife desired me to leave that to her; so I readily did, and she carried it all on with a prudence not to be disputed; and after she had wrapped my legs in flannel almost three months, she came and told me the sloop was ready and all the goods put on board. "And now, my dear," says she, "I come to tell you all the rest of my design; for," added she, "I hope you will not think I am going to kidnap you, and transport you from Virginia, as other people are transported to it, or that I am going to get you sent away and leave myself in possession of your estate; but you shall find me the same faithful, humble creature which I should have been if I had been still your slave, and not had any hopes of being your wife, and that in all my scheme which I have laid for your safety, in this new exigence, I have not proposed your going one step but where I shall go and be always with you, to assist and serve you on all occasions, and to take my portion with you, of what kind soever our lot may be."

This was so generous, and so handsome a declaration of her fidelity, and so great a token, too, of the goodness of her judgment in considering of the things which were before her, and of what my present circumstances called for, that, from that time forward, I gave myself cheerfully up to her management without any hesitation in the least, and after about ten days' preparation we embarked in a large sloop of my own of about sixty tons.

I should have mentioned here that I had still my faithful tutor, as I called him, at the head of my affairs;

and, as he knew who to correspond with, and how
to manage the correspondence in England, we left all
that part to him, as I had done before; and I did this
with a full satisfaction in his ability as well as in his
integrity. It is true he had been a little chagrined
in that affair of my wife, who, as I hinted before, had
married me, after telling him, in answer to his solici-
tations, that she had a husband alive. Now, though
this was literally true, yet, as it was a secret not fit to
be opened to him, I was obliged to put him off with
other reasons, as well as I could, perhaps not much to
the purpose, and perhaps not much to his satisfaction,
so that I reckoned he looked on himself as not very
kindly used several ways. But he began to get over it,
and to be easy, especially at our going away, when he
found that the trust of everything was still left in his
hands as it was before.

When my wife had thus communicated everything
of the voyage to me, and we began to be ready to go
off, she came to me one morning, and, with her usual
cheerfulness, told me she now came to tell me the rest
of her measures for the completing my deliverance; and
this was, that while we made this trip, as she called it,
to the hot springs at Nevis, she would write to a particular friend at London, whom she could depend upon,
to try to get a pardon for a person on account of the
late rebellion, with all the circumstances which my
case was attended with, viz., of having acted nothing
among them but being three days in the place; and,
while we were thus absent, she did not question but to
have an answer, which she would direct to come so
many ways that we would be sure to have the first of
it as soon as it was possible the vessels could go and
come. And in the meantime the expense should be
very small, for she would have an answer to the grand
question first, whether it could be obtained or no; and

then an account of the expense of it, that so I might judge for myself whether I would part with the needful sum or no, before any money was disbursed on my account.

I could not but be thoroughly satisfied with her contrivance in this particular, and I had nothing to add to it but that I would not have her limit her friend so strictly, but that if he saw the way clear, and that he was sure to obtain it, he should go through stitch with it, if within the expense of two or three or four hundred pounds, and that, upon advice of its being practicable, he should have bills payable by such a person on delivery of the warrant for the thing.

To fortify this, I enclosed in her packet a letter to one of my correspondents, whom I could particularly trust, with a credit for the money, on such-an-such conditions; but the honesty and integrity of my wife's correspondence was such as prevented all the expense, and yet I had the wished-for security, as if it had been all paid, as you shall hear presently.

All these things being fixed to our minds, and all things left behind in good posture of settlement as usual, we embarked together and put to sea, having the opportunity of an English man-of-war being on the coast in pursuit of the pirates, and who was just then standing away towards the Gulf of Florida, and told us he would see us safe as far as New Providence, on the Bahama Islands.

And now having fair weather and a pleasant voyage, and my flannels taken off my legs, I must hint a little what cargo I had with me; for as my circumstances were very good in that country, so I did not go such a voyage as this, and with a particular reserve of fortunes whatever might afterwards happen, without a sufficient cargo for our support, and whatever exigence might happen.

Our sloop, as I said, was of about sixty or seventy tons; and as tobacco, which is the general produce of the country, was no merchandise at Nevis, that is to say, for a great quantity, so we carried very little, but loaded the sloop with corn, peas, meal, and some barrels of pork; and an excellent cargo it was, most of it being the produce of my own plantation. We took also a considerable sum of money with us in Spanish gold, which was, as above, not for trade, but for all events. I also ordered another sloop to be hired, and to be sent after me, loaden with the same goods, as soon as they should have advice from me that I was safe arrived.

We came to the latitude of the island of Antigua, which was very near to that of Nevis, whither we intended to go, on the eighteenth day after our passing the Capes of Virginia, but had no sight of the island; only our master said he was sure if he stood the same course as he then was, and the gale held, I say he told me he was sure he should make the island in less than five hours' sail; so he stood on fair for the islands. However, his account had failed him, for we held on all the evening, made no land, and likewise all night, when in the grey of the morning we discovered from the topmast-head a brigantine and a sloop making sail after us, at the distance of about six leagues, fair weather, and the wind fresh at S.E.

Our master soon understood what they were, and came down into the cabin to me to let me know it. I was much surprised, you may be sure, at the danger, but my poor wife took from me all the concern for myself to take care of her, for she was frighted to that degree that I thought we should [not have been able to keep life in her.

While we were thus under the first hurry and surprise of the thing, suddenly another noise from the deck called us up to look out, and that was, " Land ! land ! " The master and I—for by this time I had got out of my cabin—run upon the deck, and there we saw the state of our case very plain. The two rogues that stood after us laid on all the canvas they could carry, and crowded after us amain, but at the distance, as I have said, of about six leagues, rather more than less. On the other hand, the land discovered lay about nine leagues right ahead, so that if the pirates could get of us, so as to sail three feet for our two, it was evident they would be up with us before we could make the island. If not, we should escape them and get in ; but even then we had no great hope to do any more than to run the ship ashore to save our lives, and so, stranding our vessel, spoil both sloop and cargo.

When we were making this calculation our master came in cheerfully, and told me he had crowded on more sail, and found the sloop carried it very well, and that he did not find the rogues gained much upon us, and that especially if one of them did not, that was the sloop, he found he could go away from the brigantine as he pleased. Thus we gave them what they call a stern chase, and they worked hard to come up with us till towards noon, when on a sudden they both stood away and gave us over, to our great satisfaction you may be sure.

We did not, it seems, so easily see the occasion of our deliverance as the pirate did ; for while we went spooning away large with the wind for one of the islands, with those two spurs in our heels, that is, with the two thieves at our sterns, there lay an English man-of-war in the road of Nevis, which was the same island from whence they espied the pirates, but the land lying between, we could not see them.

As the man-of-war discovered them she immediately slipped her cable and put herself under sail in chase of the rogues; and they as soon perceived her, and being windward, put themselves upon a wind to escape her; and thus we were delivered, and in half-an-hour more we knew who was our deliverer, seeing the man-of-war stretch ahead clear of the island, and stand directly after the pirates, who now crowded from us as fast as they crowded after us before; and thus we got safe into Antigua, after the terrible apprehension we had been in of being taken. Our apprehensions of being taken now were much more than they would have been on board a loaden ship from or to London, where the most they ordinarily do is to rifle the ship, take what is valuable and portable, and let her go. But ours being but a sloop, and all our loading being good provisions, such as they wanted, to be sure, for their ship's store, they would certainly have carried us away, ship and all, taken out the cargo and the men, and perhaps have set the sloop on fire; so that, as to our cargo of gold, it had been inevitably lost, and we hurried away, nobody knows where, and used as such barbarous fellows are wont to use innocent people as fall into their hands.

But we were now out of their hands, and had the satisfaction a few days after to hear that the man-of-war pursued them so close, notwithstanding they changed their course in the night, that the next day they were obliged to separate and shift for themselves; so the man-of-war took one of them, namely, the brigantine, and carried her into Jamaica, but the other, viz., the sloop, made her escape.

Being arrived here, we presently disposed of our cargo, and at a tolerable good price; and now the question was, what I should do next. I looked upon myself to be safe here from the fears I had been under of being discovered as a rebel, and so indeed I was; but having been now absent five months, and having sent the ship back with a cargo of rum and molasses, which I knew was wanting in my plantations, I received the same vessel back in return loaden, as at first, with provisions.

With this cargo my wife received a packet from London from the person whom she had employed, as above, to solicit a pardon, who very honestly wrote to her that he would not be so unjust to her friend, whoever he was, as to put him to any expense for a private solicitation; for that he was very well assured that his Majesty had resolved, from his own native disposition to acts of clemency and mercy to his subjects, to grant a general pardon, with some few exceptions to persons extraordinary, and he hoped her friend was none of the extraordinary persons to be excepted.

This was a kind of life from the dead to us both, and it was resolved that my wife should go back in the sloop directly to Virginia, where she should wait the good news from England, and should send me an account of it as soon as she received it.

Accordingly she went back, and came safe with the sloop and cargo to our plantation, from whence, after above four months' more expectation, behold the sloop came to me again, but empty and gutted of all her cargo, except about a hundred sacks of unground malt, which the pirates, not knowing how to brew, knew not what to do with, and so had left in her. However, to my infinite satisfaction, there was a packet of letters from my wife, with another to her from England, as well one from her friend as one from my own correspondent; both of them intimating that the king had signed an act of grace, that is to say, a general free pardon, and sent me copies of the act, wherein it was manifest that I was fully included.

And here let me hint, that having now, as it were,

received my life at the hands of King George, and in a manner so satisfying as it was to me, it made a generous convert of me, and I became sincerely given in to the interest of King George; and this from a principle of gratitude and a sense of my obligation to his Majesty for my life; and it has continued ever since, and will certainly remain with me as long as any sense of honour and of the debt of gratitude remains with me. I mention this to hint how far in such cases justice and duty to ourselves commands us; namely, that to those who graciously give us our lives when it is in their power to take them away, those lives are a debt ever after, and ought to be set apart for their service and interest as long as any of the powers of life remain, for gratitude is a debt that never ceases while the benefit received remains; and if my prince has given me my life, I can never pay the debt fully, unless such a circumstance as this should happen, that the prince's life should be in my power, and I as generously preserved it. And yet neither would the obligation be paid then, because the cases would differ; thus, that my preserving the life of my prince was my natural duty, whereas the prince on his side, my life being forfeited to him, had no motive but mere clemency and beneficence.

Perhaps this principle may not please all that read it; but as I have resolved to guide my actions in things of such a nature by the rules of strict virtue and principles of honour, so I must lay it down as a rule of honour, that a man having once forfeited his life to the justice of his prince and to the laws of his country, and receiving it back as a bounty from the grace of his sovereign, such a man can never lift up his hand again against that prince without a forfeiture of his virtue and an irreparable breach of his honour and duty, and deserves no pardon after it either from God or man.

But all this is a digression: I leave it as a sketch of the laws of honour, printed by the laws of nature in the breast of a soldier or a man of honour, and which, I believe, all impartial persons who understand what honour means will subscribe to.

But I return now to my present circumstances. My wife was gone, and with her all my good fortune and success in business seemed to have forsaken me; and I had another scene of misery to go through, after I had thought that all my misfortunes were over and at an end.

My sloop, as I have told you, arrived, but having met with a pirate rogue in the Gulf of Florida, they took her first; then finding her cargo to be all eatables, which they always want, they gutted her of all her loading, except, as I have said, about a hundred sacks of malt, which they really knew not what to do with; and, which was still worse, they took away all the men except the master and two boys, who they left on board just to run the vessel into Antigua, where they said they were bound.

But the most valuable part of my cargo, viz., a packet of letters from England, those they left, to my inexpressible comfort and satisfaction; and, particularly, that by those I saw my way home to return to my wife and to my plantations, from which I promised myself never to wander any more.

In order to this, I now embarked myself and all my effects on board the sloop, resolving to sail directly to the Capes of Virginia. My captain beating it up to reach the Bahama channel, had not been two days at sea but we were overtaken by a violent storm, which drove us so far upon the coast of Florida as that we twice struck upon the shore, and had we struck a third time we had been inevitably lost. A day or two after that, the storm abating a little, we kept the sea, but found the wind blowing so strong against our passing the gulf, and the sea going so high, we could not hold it any longer. So we were forced to bear away and make what shift we could; in which distress, the fifth day after, we made land, but found it to be Cape ———, the north-west part of the isle of Cuba. Here we found ourselves under a necessity to run in under the land for shelter, though we had not come to an anchor, so we had not touched the king of Spain's territories at all. However, in the morning we were surrounded with five Spanish barks, or boats, such as they call *barco longos*, full of men, who instantly boarded us, took us and carried us into the Havannah, the most considerable port belonging to the Spaniards in that part of the world.

Here the sloop was immediately seized, and in consequence plundered, as any one that knows the Spaniards, especially in that country, will easily guess. Our men were made prisoners and sent to the common gaol; and as for myself and the captain, we were carried before the Alcade Major, or intendant of the place, as criminals.

I spoke Spanish very well, having served under the king of Spain in Italy, and it stood me in good stead at this time; for I so effectually argued the injustice of their treatment of me that the governor, or what I ought to call him, frankly owned they ought not to have stopped me, seeing I was in the open sea pursuing my voyage, and offered no offence to anybody, and had not landed or offered to land upon any part of his Catholic Majesty's dominions till I was brought as a prisoner.

It was a great favour that I could obtain thus much; but I found it easier to obtain an acknowledgment that I had received wrong than to get any satisfaction for that wrong, and much less was there any hope or prospect of restitution; and I was let know that I was to wait till an account could be sent to the viceroy of Mexico, and orders could be received back from him how to act in the affair.

I could easily foresee what all this tended to, namely, to a confiscation of the ship and goods by the ordinary process at the place; and that my being left to the decision of the viceroy of Mexico was but a pretended representation of things to him from the corregidore or judge of the place.

However, I had no remedy but the old insignificant thing called patience, and this I was better furnished with because I did not so much value the loss as I made them believe I did. My greatest apprehensions were that they would detain me and keep me as a prisoner for life, and perhaps send me to their mines in Peru, as they have done many, and pretended to do to all that come on shore in their dominions, how great soever the distresses may have been which have brought them thither, and which has been the reason why others who have been forced on shore have committed all manner of violence upon the Spaniards in their turn, resolving, however dear they sold their lives, not to fall into their hands.

But I got better quarter among them than that too, which was, as I have said, much of it owing to my speaking Spanish, and to my telling them how I had fought in so many occasions in the quarrel of his Catholic Majesty in Italy; and, by great good chance, I had the king of France's commission for lieutenant-colonel in the Irish brigade in my pocket, where it was mentioned that the said brigade was then serving in the armies of France, under the orders of his Catholic Majesty, in Italy.

I failed not to talk up the gallantry and personal bravery of his Catholic Majesty on all occasions, and particularly in many battles where, by the way, his

Majesty had never been at all, and in some where I had never been myself. But I found I talked to people who knew nothing of the matter, and so anything went down with them if it did but praise the king of Spain and talk big of the Spanish cavalry, of which, God knows, there was not one regiment in the army, at least while I was there.

However, this way of managing myself obtained me the liberty of the place, upon my parole that I would not attempt an escape; and I obtained also, which was a great favour, to have two hundred pieces of eight allowed me out of the sale of my cargo for subsistence till I could negotiate my affairs at Mexico. As for my men, they were maintained as prisoners at the public charge.

Well, after several months' solicitation and attendance, all I could obtain was the satisfaction of seeing my ship and cargo confiscated and my poor sailors in a fair way to be sent to the mines. The last I begged off, upon condition of paying three hundred pieces of eight for their ransom, and having them set on shore at Antigua, and myself to remain hostage for the payment of the said three hundred pieces of eight, and for two hundred pieces of eight, which I had already had, and for five hundred pieces of eight more for my own ransom, if, upon a return from Mexico, the sentence of confiscation, as above, should be confirmed by the viceroy.

These were hard articles indeed, but I was forced to submit to them; nor, as my circumstances were above all such matters as these, as to substance, did I lay it much to heart. The greatest difficulty that lay in my way was, that I knew not how to correspond with my friends in any part of the world, or which way to supply myself with necessaries or with money for the payment I had agreed to, the Spaniards being so tenacious of their ports that they allowed nobody to come on shore, or indeed near the shore, from any part of the world, upon pain of seizure and confiscation, as had been my case already.    Upon this difficulty I began to reason with the corregidore, and tell him that he put things upon us that were impossible, and that were inconsistent with the customs of nations ; that, if a man was prisoner at Algiers, they would allow him to write to his friends to pay his ransom, and would admit the person that brought it to come and go free as a public person, and if they did not, no treaty could be carried on for the ransom of a slave, nor the conditions be performed when they are agreed upon.

I brought it then down to my own case, and desired to know, upon supposition, that I might, within the time limited in that agreement, have the sums of money ready for the ransom of my men and of myself, how I should obtain to have notice given me of it, or how it should be brought, seeing the very persons bringing that notice, or afterwards presuming to bring the money, might be liable to be seized and confiscated, as I had been, and the money itself be taken as a second prize, without redeeming the first.

Though this was so reasonable a request that it could not be withstood in point of argument, yet the Spaniard shrunk his head into his shoulders, and said they had not power sufficient to act in such a case ; that the king's laws were so severe against the suffering any strangers to set their foot on his Catholic Majesty's dominions in America, and they could not dispense with the least tittle of them without a particular *assiento*, as they called it, from the Consulado, or Chamber of Commerce, at Seville, or a command under the hand and seal of the viceroy of Mexico.

" How ! signior corregidore," said I, with some

warmth, and, as it were, with astonishment, "have you not authority enough to sign a passport for an agent, or ambassador, to come on shore here, from any of the king of Great Britain's governors in these parts, under a white flag, or flag of truce, to speak with the governor of this place, or with any other person in the king's name, on the subject of such business as the governor may have to communicate? Why," said I, "if you cannot do that, you cannot act according to the law of nations."

He shook his head, but still said no, he could not do even so much as that; but here one of the military governors put in and opposed him, and they two differed warmly, the first insisting that their orders were deficient in that particular; but the other said that, as they were bound up to them, it could not be in their power to act otherwise, and that they were answerable for the ill consequences.

"Well, then," says the governor to the corregidore, "now you have kept this Englishman as hostage for the ransom of the men that you have dismissed, suppose he tells you the money is ready, either at such, or such, or such a place, how shall he bring it hither? You will take all the people prisoners that offer to bring it; what must he do? If you say you will send and fetch it, what security shall he have that he shall have his liberty when it is paid you? and why should he trust you so far as to pay the money, and yet remain here a prisoner?"

This carried so much reason with it that the corregidore knew not what to say, but that so was the law, and he could act no otherwise but by the very letter of it; and here each was so positive that nothing could determine it but another express to be sent to the viceroy of Mexico.

Upon this the governor was so kind as to say he

would get me a passport for anybody that should bring
the money, and any vessel they were in, by his own
authority, and for their safe returning, and taking me
with them, provided I would answer for it that they
should bring no European or other goods whatever with
them, and should not set foot on shore without his
express permission, and provided he did not receive
orders to the contrary, in the meantime, from any
superior hand ; and that, even in such a case, they
should have liberty to go back freely from whence they
came, under the protection of a white flag.

I bowed very respectfully to the governor in token
of my acknowledging his justice, and then presented
my humble petition to him that he would allow my
men to take their own sloop ; that it should be rated at
a certain value, and would be obliged they should bring
specie on board with them, and that they should either
pay it for the sloop or leave the sloop again.

Then he inquired to what country he would send
them for so much money, and if I could assure him of
the payment ; and when he understood it was no farther
than to Virginia he seemed very easy ; and, to satisfy
the corregidore, who still stood off, adhering with a
true Spanish stiffness to the letter of the law, the said
governor calls out to me : " Signior," says he, " I shall
make all this matter easy to you, if you agree to my
proposal. Your men shall have the sloop, on condition
you shall be my hostage for her return ; but they shall
not take her as your sloop, though she shall in the effect
be yours on the payment of the money ; but you shall
take two of my men on board with you, upon your
parole for their safe return, and when she returns she
shall carry his Catholic Majesty's colours, and be entered
as one of the sloops belonging to the Havannah ; one
of the Spaniards to be commander, and to be called by
such a name as he shall appoint."

This the corregidore came into immediately, and said this was within the letter of the king's commanderie or precept; upon condition, however, that she should bring no European goods on board. I desired it might be put in other words; namely, that she should bring no European goods on shore. It cost two days' debate between these two whether it should pass that no European goods should be brought in the ship or brought on shore; but having found means to intimate that I meant not to trade there, but would not be tied from bringing a small present to a certain person in acknowledgment of favours—I say, after I had found room to place such a hint right where it should be placed, I found it was all made easy to me; and it was all agreed presently that, after the ransom was paid, and the ship also bought, it was but reasonable that I should have liberty to trade to any other country not in the dominions of the king of Spain, so to make up my losses; and that it would be hard to oblige my men to bring away the vessel light, and so lose the voyage, and add so much to our former misfortunes; that, so long as no goods were brought on shore in the country belonging to his Catholic Majesty's dominions, which was all that they had to defend, the rest was no business of theirs.

Now I began to see my way through this unhappy business, and to find, that as money would bring me out of it, so money would bring it to turn to a good account another way. Wherefore I sent the sloop away under Spanish colours, and called her the *Nuestra Signiora de la Val de Grace*, commanded by Signior Giraldo de Nesma, one of the two Spaniards.

With the sloop I sent letters to my wife and to my chief manager with orders to load her back, as I there directed, viz., that she should have two hundred barrels of flour, fifty barrels of pease; and, to answer my other views, I ordered a hundred bales to be made up of all sorts of European goods, such as not my own warehouses only would supply, but such as they could be supplied with in other warehouses where I knew they had credit for anything.

In this cargo I directed all the richest and most valuable English goods they had, or could get, whether linen, woollen, or silk, to be made up; the coarser things, such as we use in Virginia for clothing of servants, such I ordered to be left behind for the use of the plantation. In less than seven weeks' time the sloop returned, and I, that failed not every day to look out for her on the strand, was the first that spied her at sea at a distance, and knew her by her sails, but afterwards more particularly by her signals.

When she returned she came into the road with her Spanish ancient flying, and came to an anchor as directed; but I, that had seen her some hours before, went directly to the governor and gave him an account of her being come, and fain I would have obtained the favour to have his excellency, as I called him, go on board in person, that he might see how well his orders were executed. But he declined that, saying he could not justify going off of the island, which was, in short, to go out of his command of the fort, which he could not reassume without a new commission from the king's own hand.

Then I asked leave to go on board myself, which he granted me; and I brought on shore with me the full sum in gold which I had conditioned to pay for the ransom both of my men and myself, and for the purchase of the sloop; and as I obtained leave to land in a different place, so my governor sent his son with six soldiers to receive and convey me with the money to the castle, where he commanded, and therein to his own house. I had made up the money in heavy parcels, as if it had been all silver, and gave it to two of my men who belonged to the sloop, with orders to them that they should make it seem, by their carrying it, to be much heavier than it was. This was done to conceal three parcels of goods which I had packed up with the money to make a present to the governor as I intended.

When the money was carried in and laid down on a table, the governor ordered my men to withdraw, and I gave the soldiers each of them a piece of eight to drink, for which they were very thankful, and the governor seemed well pleased with it also. Then I asked him presently if he would please to receive the money. He said no, he would not receive it but in presence of the corregidore and the other people concerned. Then I begged his excellency, as I called him, to give me leave to open the parcels in his presence, for that I would do myself the honour to acknowledge his favours in the best manner I could.

He told me no, he could not see anything be brought on shore but the money; but, if I had brought anything on shore for my own use, he would not be so strict as to inquire into that, so I might do what I pleased myself.

Upon that I went into the place, shut myself in, and having opened all the things, placed them to my mind. There was five little parcels, as follows :—

1, 2. A piece of twenty yards fine English broadcloth, five yards black, five yards crimson, in one parcel; and the rest of fine mixtures in another parcel.

3. A piece of thirty ells of fine holland linen.

4. A piece of eighteen yards of fine English brocaded silk.

5. A piece of black Colchester bays.

After I had placed these by themselves, I found means, with some seeming difficulties and much grimace, to bring him to know that this was intended for a present to himself. After all that part was over, and he had seemed to accept them, he signified, after walking a hundred turns and more in the room by them, by throwing his hat, which was under his arm, upon them, and making a very stiff bow; I say, after this he seemed to take his leave of me for a while, and I waited in an outer room. When I was called in again, I found that he had looked over all the particulars, and caused them to be removed out of the place.

But when I came again I found him quite another man. He thanked me for my present; told me it was a present fit to be given to a viceroy of Mexico rather than to a mere governor of a fort; that he had done me no services suitable to such a return, but that he would see if he could not oblige me further before I left the place.

After our compliments were over I obtained leave to have the corregidore sent for, who accordingly came, and in his presence the money stipulated for the ransom of the ship and of the men was paid.

But here the corregidore showed that he would be as severely just on my side as on theirs, for he would not admit the money as a ransom for us as prisoners, but as a deposit for so much as we were to be ransomed for if the sentence of our being made prisoners should be confirmed.

And then the governor and corregidore, joining together, sent a representation of the whole affair—at least we were told so—to the viceroy of Mexico; and it was privately hinted to me that I would do well to stay for the return of the *aviso*—that is, a boat which they send over the bay to Vera Cruz with an express to Mexico, whose return is generally performed in two months.

I was not unwilling to stay, having secret hints given me that I should find some way to go with my sloop towards Vera Cruz myself, where I might have an occasion to trade privately for the cargo which I had on board. But it came about a nearer way; for, about two days after this money being deposited, as above, the governor's son invited himself on board my sloop, where I told him I would be very glad to see him, and whither, at the same time, he brought with him three considerable merchants, Spaniards, two of them not inhabitants of the place.

When they were on board they were very merry and pleasant, and I treated them so much to their satisfaction that, in short, they were not well able to go on shore for that night, but were content to take a nap on some carpets, which I caused to be spread for them; and that the governor's son might think himself well used, I brought him a very good silk nightgown, with a crimson velvet cap, to lie down in, and in the morning desired him to accept of them for his use, which he took very kindly.

During that merry evening one of the merchants, not so touched with drink as the young gentleman, nor so as not to mind what it was he came about, takes an occasion to withdraw out of the great cabin and enter into a parley with the master of the sloop in order to trade for what European goods we had on board. The master took the hint, and gave me notice of what had passed, and I gave him instructions what to say and what to do; according to which instructions they made but few words, bought the goods for about five thousand pieces of eight, and carried them away themselves, and at their own hazards.

This was very agreeable to me, for now I began to

see I should lick myself whole by the sale of this
cargo, and should make myself full amends of Jack
Spaniard for all the injuries he had done me in the
first of these things.  With this view I gave my
master or captain of the sloop instructions for sale of
all the rest of the goods, and left him to manage by
himself, which he did so well that he sold the whole
cargo the next day to the three Spaniards ; with this
additional circumstance, that they desired the sloop
might carry the goods, as they were on board, to such
part of the *terra firma* as they should appoint between
the Honduras and the coast of La Vera Cruz.

It was difficult for me to make good this part of the
bargain, but finding the price agreed for would very
well answer the voyage, I consented.  But then how to
send the sloop away and remain among the Spaniards
when I was now a clear man, this was a difficulty too,
as it was also to go away, and not wait for a favourable
answer from the viceroy of Mexico to the representation of the governor and the corregidore.  However, at
last I resolved to go in the sloop, fall out what would ;
so I went to the governor and represented to him that,
being now to expect a favourable answer from Mexico,
it would be a great loss to me to keep the sloop there
all the while, and I desired his leave for me to go with
the sloop to Antigua to sell and dispose of the cargo,
which he well knew I was obliged not to bring on
shore there at the Havannah, and which would be in
danger of being spoiled by lying so long on board.
This I obtained readily, with license to come again
into the road, and, for myself only, to come on shore
in order to hear the viceroy's pleasure in my case,
which was depending.

Having thus obtained a license or passport for the
sloop and myself, I put to sea with the three Spanish
merchants on board with me.  They told me they

did not live at the Havannah, but it seems one of
them did; and some rich merchants of the Havannah, or of the parts thereabouts in the same island,
were concerned with them, for they brought on board,
that night we put to sea, a great sum of money in
pieces of eight; and, as I understood afterwards, that
these merchants bought the cargo of me, and though
they gave me a very great price for everything, yet
that they sold them again to the merchants, who they
procured on the coast of La Vera Cruz, at a prodigious advantage, so that they got above a hundred
per cent. after I had gained very sufficiently before.

We sailed from the Havannah directly for Vera
Cruz. I scrupled venturing into the port at first, and
was very uneasy lest I should have another Spanish
trick put upon me; but as we sailed under Spanish
colours, they showed us such authentic papers from
the proper officers that there was no room to fear
anything.

However, when we came in sight of the Spanish
coast, I found they had a secret clandestine trade to
carry on, which, though it was secret, yet they knew
the way of it so well that it was but a mere road to
them. The case was this: we stood in close under
the shore in the night, about six leagues to the north
of the port, where two of the three merchants went on
shore in the boat, and in three hours or thereabouts
they came on board again with five canoes and seven
or eight merchants more with them, and as soon as
they were on board we stood off to sea, so that by
daylight we were quite out of sight of land.

I ought to have mentioned before that as soon as we
were put to sea from the Havannah, and during our
voyage into the Gulf of Mexico, which was eight
days, we rummaged the whole cargo, and opening
every bale as far as the Spanish merchants desired, we

trafficked with them for the whole cargo, except the barrels of flour and pease.

This cargo was considerable in itself, for my wife's account or invoice, drawn out by my tutor and manager, amounted to £2684, 10s., and I sold the whole, including what had been sold in the evening, when they were on board first, as I have said, for thirty-eight thousand five hundred and ninety-three pieces of eight, and they allowed me twelve hundred pieces of eight for the freight of the sloop, and made my master and the seamen very handsome presents besides ; and they were well able to do this too, as you shall hear presently.

After we were gotten out of sight of land the Spaniards fell to their traffic, and our three merchants opened their shop, as they might say, for it was their shop. As to me, I had nothing to do with it or with their goods. They drove their bargain in a few hours, and at night we stood in again for the shore, when the five canoes carried a great part of the goods on shore, and brought the money back in specie, as well for that they carried as for all the rest, and at their second voyage carried all away clear, leaving me nothing on board but my barrels of flour and pease, which they bade me money for too, but not so much as I expected.

Here I found that my Spanish merchants made above seventy thousand pieces of eight of the cargo I had sold them, upon which I had a great mind to be acquainted with those merchants on the *terra firma*, who were the last customers ; for it presently occurred to me that I could easily go with a sloop from Virginia, and taking a cargo directed on purpose from England of about £5000 or £6000, I might easily make four of one. With this view I began to make a kind of an acquaintance with the Spaniards which came in the canoes, and we became so intimate that at last, with the consent of the three Spaniards of the Havannah, I accepted an invitation on shore to their house, which was a little villa, or rather plantation, where they had an *ingenio*, that is to say, a sugar-house, or sugar-work, and there they treated us like princes.

I took occasion at this invitation to say that, if I knew how to find my way thither again, I could visit them once or twice a year, very much to their advantage and mine too. One of the Spaniards took the hint, and taking me into a room by myself, " Seignior," says he, " if you have any thoughts of coming to this place again, I shall give you such directions as you shall be sure not to mistake ; and, upon either coming on shore in the night and coming up to this place, or upon making the signals which we shall give you, we will not fail to come off to you, and bring money enough for any *cargaison*" (so they call it) "that you shall bring."

I took all their directions, took their paroles of honour for my safety, and, without taking any notice to my first three merchants, laid up the rest in my most secret thoughts, resolving to visit them again in as short a time as I could ; and thus having, in about five days, finished all our merchandising, we stood off to sea, and made for the island of Cuba, where I set my three Spaniards on shore with all their treasure, to their heart's content, and made the best of my way to Antigua, where, with all the despatch I could, I sold my two hundred barrels of flour, which, however, had suffered a little by the length of the voyage ; and having laden the sloop with rum, molasses, and sugar, I set sail again for the Havannah.

I was now uneasy indeed, for fear of the pirates, for I was a rich ship, having, besides goods, near forty thousand pieces of eight in silver.

When I came back to the Havannah, I went on shore to wait on the governor and the corregidore, and to hear what return was had from the viceroy, and had the good fortune to know that the viceroy had disallowed that part of the sentence which condemned us as prisoners and put a ransom on us, which he insisted could not be but in time of open war.   But as to the confiscation, he deferred it to the Chamber or Council of Commerce at Seville, and the appeal to the king, if such be preferred.

This was, in some measure, a very good piece of justice in the viceroy; for, as we had not been on shore, we could not be legally imprisoned ; and for the rest, I believe if I would have given myself the trouble to have gone to Old Spain, and have preferred my claim to both the ship and the cargo, I had recovered them also.

However, as it was, I was now a freeman without ransom, and my men were also free, so that all the money which I had deposited, as above, was returned me ; and thus I took my leave of the Havannah, and made the best of my way for Virginia, where I arrived after a year and a half's absence ; and notwithstanding all my losses, came home above forty thousand pieces of eight richer than I went out.

As to the old affair about the Preston prisoners, that was quite at an end, for the general pardon passed in Parliament made me perfectly easy, and I took no more thought about that part.   I might here very usefully observe how necessary and inseparable a companion fear is to guilt.   It was but a few months before that the face of a poor Preston transport would have frighted me out of my wits ; to avoid them I feigned myself sick, and wrapped my legs in flannel, as if I had the gout ; whereas now they were no more surprise to me, nor was I any more uneasy to see them, than I was to see any other of the servants of the plantations.

And that which was more particular than all was, that, though before I fancied every one of them would know me and remember me, and consequently betray and accuse me, now, though I was frequently among them, and saw most of them, if not all of them, one time or other, nay, though I remembered several of their faces, and even some of their names, yet there was not a man of them that ever took the least notice of me, or of having known or seen me before.

It would have been a singular satisfaction to me if I could have known so much as this of them before, and have saved me all the fatigue, hazard, and misfortune that befell me afterwards ; but man, a short-sighted creature, sees so little before him that he can neither anticipate his joys nor prevent his disasters, be they ever so little a distance from him.

I had now my head full of my West India project, and I began to make provision for it accordingly. I had a full account of what European goods were most acceptable in New Spain; and, to add to my speed, I knew that the Spaniards were in great want of European goods, the galleons from Old Spain having been delayed to an unusual length of time for the two years before. Upon this account, not having time, as I thought, to send to England for a cargo of such goods as were most proper, I resolved to load my sloop with tobacco and rum, the last I brought from Antigua, and go away to Boston in New England, and to New York, and see if I could pick up a cargo to my mind.

Accordingly, I took twenty thousand pieces of eight in money, and my sloop laden as above, and taking my wife with me, we went away. It was an odd and new thing at New England to have such a quantity of goods bought up there by a sloop from Virginia, and especially to be paid for in ready money, as I did for most of my goods; and this set all the trading heads upon the stretch, to inquire what and who I was; to which they had an immediate and direct answer, that I was a very considerable planter in Virginia, and that was all any of my men on board the sloop could tell of me, and enough too.

Well, it was the cause of much speculation among them, as I heard at second and third hands. Some said, "He is certainly going to Jamaica;" others said, "He is going to trade with the Spaniards;" others that "He is going to the South Sea and turn half merchant, half pirate, on the coast of Chili and Peru;" some one thing, some another, as the men gossips found their imaginations directed; but we went on with our business, and laid out twelve thousand pieces of eight, besides our cargo of rum and tobacco, and went from thence to New York, where we laid out the rest.

The chief of the cargo we bought here was fine English broadcloth, serges, druggets, Norwich stuffs, bays, says, and all kinds of woollen manufactures, as also linen of all sorts, a very great quantity, and near £1000 in fine silks of several sorts. Being thus freighted, I came back safe to Virginia, and with very little addition to my cargo, began to prepare for my West India voyage.

I should have mentioned that I had built upon my sloop and raised her a little, so that I had made her carry twelve guns, and fitted her up for defence; for I thought she should not be attacked and boarded by a few Spanish *barco longos*, as she was before; and I found the benefit of it afterwards, as you shall hear.

We set sail the beginning of August, and as I had twice been attacked by pirates in passing the Gulf of Florida, or among the Bahama Islands, I resolved, though it was farther about, to stand off to sea, and so keep, as I believed it would be, out of the way of them.

We passed the tropic, as near as we could guess, just where the famous Sir William Phipps fished up the silver from the Spanish plate wreck, and, standing in between the islands, kept our course W. by S., keeping under the isle of Cuba, and so running away, trade, as they call it, into the great Gulf of Mexico, leaving the island of Jamaica to the S. and S.E., by this means avoiding, as I thought, all the Spaniards of Cuba or the Havannah.

As we passed the west point of Cuba three Spanish boats came off to board us, as they had done before, on the other side of the island. But they found themselves mistaken; we were too many for them, for we run out our guns, which they did not perceive before, and firing three or four shots at them, they retired.

The next morning they appeared again, being five large boats and a barque, and gave us chase; but we then spread our Spanish colours, and brought to to fight them, at which they retired; so we escaped this danger by the addition of force which we had made to our vessel.

We now had a fair run for our port, and as I had taken very good directions, I stood away to the north of St John d'Ulva, and then running in for the shore, found the place appointed exactly; and going on shore, I sent the master of my sloop directly to the *ingenio*, where he found the Spanish merchant at his house, and where he dwelt like a sovereign prince, who welcomed him, and understanding that I was in a particular boat at the creek, as appointed, he came immediately with him, and bringing another Spaniard from a villa not far off, in about four hours they were with me.

They would have persuaded me to go up to their houses and have stayed there till the next night, ordering the sloop to stand off as usual, but I would not consent to let the sloop go to sea without me, so we went on board directly, and, as the night was almost run, stood off to sea; so by daybreak we were quite out of sight of land.

Here we began, as I said before, to open shop, and I found the Spaniards were extremely surprised at seeing such a cargo—I mean so large; for, in short, they had cared not if it had been four times as much. They soon ran through the contents of all the bales we opened that night, and, with very little dispute about the price, they approved and accepted all that I showed them; but as they said they had not money for any greater parcel, they agreed to go on shore the next evening for more money.

However, we spent the remainder of the night in looking over and making inventories or invoices of the rest of the cargo, that so they might see the goods, know the value, and know what more money they had to bring.

Accordingly, in the evening we stood in for the shore, and they carried part of the cargo with them, borrowing the sloop's boat to assist them; and after they had lodged and landed the goods they came on board again, bringing three of the other merchants with them who were concerned before, and money enough to clear the whole ship—ay, and ship and all, if I had been willing to sell her.

To give them their due, they dealt with me like men of honour. They were indeed sensible that they bought everything much cheaper of me than they did before of the three merchants of the Havannah, these merchants having been, as it were, the hucksters, and bought them first of me, and then advanced, as I have said, above one hundred per cent. upon the price they gave me. But yet, at the same time, I advanced in the

price much more now than I did before to the said
Spaniards; nor was it without reason, because of the
length and risk of the voyage, both out and home,
which now lay wholly upon me.

In short, I sold the whole cargo to them, and for
which I received near two hundred thousand pieces of
eight in money; besides which, when they came on
board the second time, they brought all their boats
loaden with fresh provisions, hogs, sheep, fowls, sweetmeats, &c., enough for my whole voyage, all which
they made a present of to me. And thus we finished
our traffic to our mutual satisfaction, and parted with
promises of further commerce, and with assurances on
their part of all acts of friendship and assistance that I
could desire if any disaster should befall me in any of
these adventures—as indeed was not improbable, considering the strictness and severity of their customs in
case any people were trading upon their coast.

I immediately called a council with my little crew
which way we should go back. The mate was for
beating it up to windward and getting up to Jamaica;
but as we were too rich to run any risks, and were to
take the best course to get safe home, I thought, and
so did the master of the sloop, that our best way was
to coast about the bay, and, keeping the shore of
Florida on board, make the shortest course to the gulf,
and so make for the coast of Carolina, and to put in
there into the first port we could, and wait for any
English men-of-war that might be on the coast to
secure us to the capes.

This was the best course we could take, and proved
very safe to us, excepting that, about the cape of
Florida, and on the coast in the gulf, till we came to
the height of St Augustine, we were several times
visited with the Spaniards' *barco longos* and small
barks, in hopes of making a prize of us; but carrying

Spanish colours deceived most of them, and a good tier of guns kept the rest at a distance, so that we came safe, though once or twice in danger of being run on shore by a storm of wind—I say, we came safe into Charles River in Carolina.

From hence I found means to send a letter home, with an account to my wife of my good success; and having an account that the coast was clear of pirates, though there were no men-of-war in the place, I ventured forward, and, in short, got safe into the Bay of Chesapeake, that is to say, within the capes of Virginia, and in a few days more to my own house, having been absent three months and four days.

Never did any vessel on this side the world make a better voyage in so short a time than I made in this sloop; for by the most moderate computation I cleared in these three months £25,000 sterling in ready money, all the charges of the voyages to New England also being reckoned up.

Now was my time to have sat still, contented with what I had got, if it was in the power of man to know when his good fortune was at the highest. And more, my prudent wife gave it as her opinion that I should sit down satisfied and push the affair no farther, and earnestly persuaded me to do so. But I, that had a door open, as I thought, to immense treasure, that had found the way to have a stream of the golden rivers of Mexico flow into my plantation of Virginia, and saw no hazards more than what were common to all such things in the prosecution—I say, to me these things looked with another face, and I dreamed of nothing but millions and hundreds of thousands; so, contrary to all moderate measures, I pushed on for another voyage, and laid up a stock of all sorts of goods that I could get together proper for the trade. I did not indeed go again to New England, for I had by this time a very good cargo come from England pursuant to a commission I had sent several months before ; so that, in short, my cargo, according to the invoice now made out, amounted to above £10,000 sterling first cost, and was a cargo so sorted and so well bought that I expected to have advanced upon them much more in proportion than I had done in the cargo before.

With these expectations we began our second voyage in April, being about five months after our return from the first. We had not indeed the same good speed, even in our beginning, as we had at first ; for though we stood off to sea about sixty leagues in order to be out of the way of the pirates, yet we had not been above five days at sea but we were visited and rifled by two pirate barks, who, being bound to the northward, that is to say, the banks of Newfoundland, took away all our provisions and all our ammunition and small arms, and left us very ill provided to pursue our voyage ; and it being so near home, we thought it advisable to come about and stand in for the capes again, to restore our condition and furnish ourselves with stores of all kinds for our voyage. This took us up about ten days, and we put to sea again. As for our cargo, the pirates did not meddle with it, being all bale goods, which they had no present use for, and knew not what to do with if they had them.

We met with no other adventure worth naming till, by the same course that we had steered before, we came into the Gulf of Mexico ; and the first misfortune we met with here was, that, on the back of Cuba, crossing towards the point of the *terra firma*, on the coast of Yucatan, we had sight of the flota of New Spain, that is, of the ships which come from Carthagena or Porto Bello, and go to the Havannah, in order to pursue their voyage to Europe.

They had with them one Spanish man-of-war and

three frigates. Two of the frigates gave us chase ; but, it being just at the shutting in of the day, we soon lost sight of them, and standing to the north, across the Bay of Mexico, as if we were going to the mouth of Mississippi, they lost us quite, and in a few days more we made the bottom of the bay, being the port we were bound for.

We stood in as usual in the night, and gave notice to our friends ; but instead of their former readiness to come on board, they gave us notice that we had been seen in the bay, and that notice of us was given at Vera Cruz and at other places, and that several frigates were in quest of us, and that three more would be cruising the next morning in search for us. We could not conceive how this could be ; but we were afterwards told that those three frigates, having lost sight of us in the night, had made in for the shore, and had given the alarm of us as of privateers.

Be that as it would, we had nothing to do but to consider what course to take immediately. The Spanish merchants' advice was very good if we had taken it, namely, to have unladen as many of our bales as we could that very night by the help of our boat and their canoes, and to make the best of our way in the morning to the north of the gulf, and take our fate.

This my skipper or master thought very well of, but when we began to put it into execution, we were so confused and in such a hurry, being not resolved what course to take, that we could not get out above sixteen bales of all sorts of goods before it began to be too light and it behoved us to sail. At last the master proposed a medium, which was, that I should go on shore in the next boat, in which were five bales of goods more, and that I should stay on shore if the Spanish merchants would undertake to conceal me, and let them go to sea and take their chance.

The Spanish merchants readily undertook to protect me, especially it being so easy to have me pass for a natural Spaniard, and so they took me on shore with twenty-one bales of my goods, and the sloop stood off to sea. If they met with any enemies they were to stand in for the shore the next night; and we failed not to look well out for them, but to no purpose, for the next day they were discovered and chased by two Spanish frigates. They stood from them, and the sloop, being an excellent sailer, gained so much that they would certainly have been clear of them when night came on, but a small picaroon of a sloop kept them company in spite of all they could do, and two or three times offered to engage them, thereby to give time to the rest to come up; but the sloop kept her way, and gave them a chase of three days and nights, having a fresh gale of wind at S.W., till she made the Rio Grand, or, as the French call it, the Mississippi, and there finding no remedy, they ran the vessel on shore not far from the fort which the Spaniards call Pensacola, garrisoned at that time with French. Our men would have entered the river as a port, but having no pilot, and the current of the river being strong against them, the sloop ran on shore, and the men shifted as well as they could in their boats.

I was now in a very odd condition indeed. My circumstances were in one sense, indeed, very happy —namely, that I was in the hands of my friends, for such really they were, and so faithful that no men could have been more careful of their own safety than were they of mine; and that which added to the comfort of my new condition was the produce of my goods, which were gotten on shore by their own advice and direction, which was a fund sufficient to maintain me with them as long as I could be supposed to stay there; and if not, the first merchant to whose house I went assured me that he would give me credit for twenty thousand pieces of eight if I had occasion for it.

My greatest affliction was, that I knew not how to convey news to my wife of my present condition, and how, among many misfortunes of the voyage, I was yet safe and in good hands.

But there was no remedy for this part but the great universal cure of all incurable sorrows, viz., patience ; and, indeed, I had a great deal of reason, not for patience only, but thankfulness, if I had known the circumstances which I should have been reduced to if I had fallen into the hands of the Spaniards ; the best of which that I could reasonably have expected had been to have been sent to the mines, or, which was ten thousand times worse, the Inquisition ; or, if I had escaped the Spaniards, as my men in the sloop did, the hardships they were exposed to, the dangers they were in, and the miseries they suffered were still worse in wandering among savages, and the more savage French, who plundered and stripped them, instead of relieving and supplying them in their long wilderness journey over the mountains till they reached the S.W. parts of South Carolina, a journey which, indeed, deserves to have an account to be given of it by itself. I say, all these things, had I known of them, would have let me see that I had a great deal of reason, not only to be patient under my present circumstances, but satisfied and thankful.

Here, as I said, my patron, the merchant, entertained me like a prince ; he made my safety his peculiar care, and while we were in any expectation of the sloop being taken and brought into Vera Cruz, he kept me retired at a little house in a wood, where he kept a fine aviary of all sorts of American birds, and out of which he yearly sent some as presents to his friends in Old Spain.

This retreat was necessary lest, if the sloop should be taken and brought into Vera Cruz, and the men be brought in prisoners, they should be tempted to give an account of me as their supercargo or merchant, and where both I and the twenty-one bales of goods were set on shore. As for the goods, he made sure work with them, for they were all opened, taken out of the bales, and separated, and, being mixed with other European goods which came by the galleons, were made up in new package, and sent to Mexico in several parcels, some to one merchant, some to another, so that it was impossible to have found them out, even if they had had information of them.

In this posture, and in apprehension of some bad news of the sloop, I remained at the villa, or house in the vale—for so they called it—about five weeks. I had two negroes appointed to wait on me, one of which was my purveyor, or my cook, the other my valet; and my friend, the master of all, came constantly every evening to visit and sup with me, when we walked out together into the aviary, which was, of its kind, the most beautiful thing that ever I saw in the world.

After above five weeks' retreat of this kind, he had good intelligence of the fate of the sloop, viz., that the two frigates and a sloop had chased her till she ran on ground near the fort of Pensacola; that they saw her stranded and broke in pieces by the force of the waves, the men making their escape in their boat. This news was brought, it seems, by the said frigates to La Vera Cruz, where my friend went on purpose to be fully informed, and received the account from one of the captains of the frigates, and discoursed with him at large about it.

I was better pleased with the loss of the sloop and all my cargo, the men being got on shore and escaping, than I should have been with the saving the whole cargo, if the men had fallen into the hands of the Spaniards; for now I was safe, whereas then, it being supposed they would have been forced to some discovery about me, I must have fled, and should have found it very difficult to have made my escape, even with all that my friends could have done for me too.

But now I was perfectly easy, and my friend, who thought confining me at the house in the vale no longer needful, brought me publicly home to his dwelling-house, as a merchant come from Old Spain by the last galleons, and who, having been at Mexico, was come to reside with him.

Here I was dressed like a Spaniard of the better sort, had three negroes to attend me, and was called Don Ferdinand de Villa Moresa, in Castilia Feja— that is to say, in Old Castile.

Here I had nothing to do but to walk about and ride out into the woods, and come home again to enjoy the pleasantest and most agreeable retirement in the world; for certainly no men in the world live in such splendour and wallow in such immense treasures as the merchants of this place.

They live, as I have said, in a kind of country retreat at their villas, or, as we would call them in Virginia, their plantations, and, as they do call them, their *ingenios*, where they make their indigo and their sugars. But they have also houses and warehouses at Vera Cruz, where they go twice a year, when the galleons arrive from Old Spain, and when those galleons re-lade for their return. And it was surprising to me, when I went to La Vera Cruz with them, to see what prodigious consignments they had from their correspondents in Old Spain, and with what despatch they managed them; for no sooner were the cases, packs, and bales of European goods brought into their warehouses but they were opened and repacked by porters and packers of their own—that is to say, negroes and Indian servants—and being made up into new bales and separate parcels, were all despatched again by horses for Mexico, and directed to their several merchants there, and the remainder carried home, as above, to the *ingenio* where they lived, which was near thirty English miles from Vera Cruz, so that in about twenty days their warehouses were again entirely free. At La Vera Cruz, all their business was over there, and they and all their servants retired ; for they stayed no longer there than needs must, because of the unhealthiness of the air.

After the goods were thus despatched, it was equally surprising to see how soon, and with what exactness, the merchants of Mexico to whom those cargoes were separately consigned made the return, and how it came all in silver or in gold, so that their warehouses in a few months were piled up, even to the ceiling, with chests of pieces of eight and with bars of silver.

It is impossible to describe in the narrow compass of this work with what exactness and order, and yet with how little hurry, and not the least confusion, everything was done, and how soon a weight of business of such importance and value was negotiated and finished, the goods repacked, invoices made, and everything despatched and gone ; so that in about five weeks all the goods they had received from Europe by the galleons were disposed of and entered in their journals to the proper account of their merchant to whom they were respectively consigned ; from thence they had book-keepers who drew out the invoices and wrote the letters, which the merchant himself only read over and signed, and then other hands copied all again into other books.

I can give no estimate of the value of the several consignments they received by that flota ; but I remember

that, when the galleons went back, they shipped on
board, at several times, one million three hundred thousand pieces of eight in specie, besides a hundred and
eighty bales or bags of cochineal and about three hundred bales of indigo ; but they were so modest that
they said this was for themselves and their friends.
That is to say, the several merchants of Mexico consigned large quantities of bullion to them, to ship on
board and consign according to their order ; but then
I know also that, for all that, they were allowed commission, so that their gain was very considerable even
that way also.

I had been with them at La Vera Cruz, and came
back again before we came to an account for the goods
which I had brought on shore in the twenty-one bales,
which, by the account we brought them to (leaving a
piece of everything to be governed by our last market),
amounted to eight thousand five hundred and seventy
pieces of eight, all which money my friend—for so I
must now call him—brought me in specie, and caused
his negroes to pile them up in one corner of my apartment ; so that I was indeed still very rich, all things
considered.

There was a bale which I had caused to be packed
up on purpose in Virginia, and which indeed I had
written for from England, being chiefly of fine English
broadcloths, silk, silk druggets, and fine stuffs of several
kinds, with some very fine hollands, which I set apart
for presents, as I should find occasion ; and as, whatever hurry I was in at carrying the twenty-one bales of
goods on shore, I did not forget to let this bale be one
of them, so, when we came to a sale for the rest, I told
them that this was a pack with clothes and necessaries for
my own wearing and use, and so desired it might not be
opened with the rest, which was accordingly observed,
and that bale or pack was brought into my apartment.

This bale was, in general, made up of several smaller bales, which I had directed, so that I might have room to make presents, equally sorted as the circumstance might direct me. However, they were all considerable, and I reckoned the whole bale cost me near £200 sterling in England ; and though my present circumstances required some limits to my bounty in making presents, yet the obligation I was under being so much the greater, especially to this one friendly, generous Spaniard, I thought I could not do better than, by opening two of the smaller bales, join them together, and make my gift something suitable to the benefactor, and to the respect he had shown me. Accordingly I took two bales, and, laying the goods together, the contents were as follows :—

Two pieces of fine English broadcloth, the finest that could be got in London, divided, as was that which I gave to the governor at the Havannah, into fine crimson in grain, fine light mixtures, and fine black.

Four pieces of fine holland, of 7s. to 8s. per ell in London.

Twelve pieces of fine silk drugget and duroys, for men's wear.

Six pieces of broad silks, two damasks, two brocaded silks, and two mantuas.

With a box of ribands and a box of lace ; the last cost about £40 sterling in England.

This handsome parcel I laid open in my apartment, and brought him upstairs one morning, on pretence to drink chocolate with me, which he ordinarily did ; when, as we drank chocolate and was merry, I said to him, though I had sold him almost all my cargo and taken his money, yet the truth was, that I ought not to have sold them to him, but to have laid them all at his feet, for that it was to his direction I owed the having anything saved at all.

He smiled, and, with a great deal of friendship in his face, told me that not to have paid me for them would have been to have plundered a shipwreck, which had been worse than to have robbed an hospital.

At last I told him I had two requests to make to him, which must not be denied.  I told him I had a small present to make him, which I would give him a reason why he should not refuse to accept ; and the second request I would make after the first was granted. He said he would have accepted my present from me if I had not been under a disaster, but as it was it would be cruel and ungenerous.  But I told him he was obliged to hear my reason for his accepting it. Then I told him that this parcel was made up for him by name by my wife and I in Virginia, and his name set on the marks of the bale, and accordingly I showed him the marks, which was indeed on one of the bales, but I had doubled it now, as above, so that I told him these were his own proper goods ; and, in short, I pressed him so to receive them that he made a bow ; and I said no more, but ordered my negro, that is to say, his negro that waited on me, to carry them all, except the two boxes, into his apartments, but would not let him see the particulars till they were all carried away.

After he was gone about a quarter of an hour, he came in raving and almost swearing, and in a great passion, but I could easily see he was exceedingly pleased ; and told me, had he known the particulars, he would never have suffered them to have gone as he did, and at last used the very same compliment that the governor at the Havannah used, viz., that it was a present fit for a viceroy of Mexico rather than for him.

When he had done, he then told me he remembered

I had two requests to him, and that one was not to be told till after the first was granted, and he hoped now I had something to ask of him that was equal to the obligation I laid upon him.

I told him I knew it was not the custom in Spain for a stranger to make presents to the ladies, and that I would not in the least doubt but that, whatever the ladies of his family required as proper for their use, he would appropriate to them as he thought fit ; but that there were two little boxes in the parcel which my wife with her own hand had directed to the ladies ; and I begged he would be pleased with his own hand to give them in my wife's name, as directed ; that I was only the messenger, but that I could not be honest if I did not discharge myself of the trust reposed in me.

These were the two boxes of ribands and lace, which, knowing the nicety of the ladies in Spain, or rather of the Spaniards about their women, I had made my wife pack up, and directed with her own hand, as I have said.

He smiled, and told me it was true the Spaniards did not ordinarily admit so much freedom among the women as other nations ; but he hoped, he said, I would not think the Spaniards thought all their women whores, or that all Spaniards were jealous of their wives ; that, as to my present, since he had agreed to accept of it, I should have the direction of what part I pleased to his wife and daughters ; for he had three daughters.

Here I strained courtesies again, and told him by no means ; I would direct nothing of that kind. I only begged that he would with his own hand present to his donna, or lady, the present designed her by my wife, and that he would present it in her name, now living in Virginia. He was extremely pleased with the nicety I used; and I saw him present it to her accordingly, and could see, at the opening of it, that she was extremely pleased with the present itself, as indeed might very well be, for in that country it was worth a very considerable sum of money.

Though I was used with an uncommon friendship before, and nothing could well be desired more, yet the grateful sense I showed of it in the magnificence of this present was not lost, and the whole family appeared sensible of it; so that I must allow that presents, where they can be made in such a manner, are not without their influence, where the persons were not at all mercenary either before or after.

I had here now a most happy and comfortable retreat, though it was a kind of an exile. Here I enjoyed everything I could think of that was agreeable and pleasant, except only a liberty of going home, which, for that reason perhaps, was the only thing I desired in the world; for the grief of one absent comfort is oftentimes capable of embittering all the other enjoyments in the world.

Here I enjoyed the moments which I had never before known how to employ—I mean that here I learned to look back upon a long ill-spent life, blessed with infinite advantage, which I had no heart given me till now to make use of, and here I found just reflections were the utmost felicity of human life.

Here I wrote these memoirs, having to add to the pleasure of looking back with due reflections the benefit of a violent fit of the gout, which, as it is allowed by most people, clears the head, restores the memory, and qualifies us to make the most, and just, and useful remarks upon our own actions.

Perhaps when I wrote these things down I did not foresee that the writings of our own stories would be so much the fashion in England, or so agreeable to others to read, as I find custom and the humour of the times has caused it to be.  If any one that reads my story pleases to make the same just reflections which I acknowledge I ought to have made, he will reap the benefit of my misfortunes perhaps more than I have done myself.  'Tis evident by the long series of changes and turns which have appeared in the narrow compass of one private, mean person's life, that the history of men's lives may be many ways made useful and instructing to those who read them, if moral and religious improvement and reflections are made by those that write them.

There remains many things in the course of this unhappy life of mine, though I have left so little a part of it to speak of, that is worth giving a large and distinct account of, and which gives room for just reflections of a kind which I have not made yet. Particularly, I think it just to add how, in collecting the various changes and turns in my affairs, I saw clearer than ever I had done before how an invincible overruling Power, a hand influenced from above, governs all our actions of every kind, limits all our designs, and orders the events of everything relating to us.

And from this observation it necessarily occurred to me how just it was that we should pay the homage of all events to Him ; that as He guided, and had even made the chain of cause and consequences, which nature in general strictly obeyed, so to Him should be given the honour of all events, the consequences of those causes, as the first Mover and Maker of all things.

I, who had hitherto lived, as might be truly said, without God in the world, began now to see farther into all those things than I had ever yet been capable of before, and this brought me at last to look with

shame and blushes upon such a course of wickedness
as I had gone through in the world.  I had been bred,
indeed, to nothing of either religious or moral knowledge.  What I gained of either was, first, by the little
time of civil life which I lived in Scotland, where
my abhorrence of the wickedness of my captain and
comrade, and some sober, religious company I fell
into, first gave me some knowledge of good and evil,
and showed me the beauty of a sober, religious life,
though, with my leaving that country, it soon left me
too ; or, secondly, the modest hints and just reflections
of my steward, whom I called my tutor, who was a
man of sincere religion, good principles, and a real,
true penitent for his past miscarriages.  Oh ! had I
with him sincerely repented of what was past, I had
not for twenty-four years together lived a life of levity
and profligate wickedness after it.

But here I had, as I said, leisure to reflect and to
repent, to call to mind things past, and, with a just
detestation, learn, as Job says, to abhor myself in dust
and ashes.

It is with this temper that I have written my story.
I would have all that design to read it prepare to do
so with the temper of penitents, and remember with
how much advantage they may make their penitent
reflections at home, under the merciful dispositions of
Providence, in peace, plenty, and ease, rather than
abroad, under the discipline of a transported criminal,
as my wife and my tutor, or under the miseries and
distresses of a shipwrecked wanderer, as my skipper
or captain of the sloop, who, as I hear, died a very
great penitent, labouring in the deserts and mountains
to find his way home to Virginia, by the way of
Carolina, whither the rest of the crew reached after
infinite dangers and hardships ; or in exile, however
favourably circumstanced, as mine, in absence from

my family, and for some time in no probable view of ever seeing them any more.

Such, I say, may repent with advantage ; but how few are they that seriously look in till their way is hedged up and they have no other way to look !

Here, I say, I had leisure to repent.  How far it pleases God to give the grace of repentance where He gives the opportunity of it is not for me to say of myself.  It is sufficient that I recommend it to all that read this story, that, when they find their lives come up in any degree to any similitude of cases, they will inquire by me, and ask themselves, Is not this the time to repent ?  Perhaps the answer may touch them.

I have only to add to what was then written, that my kind friends the Spaniards, finding no other method presented for conveying me to my home—that is to say, to Virginia—got a license for me to come in the next galleons, as a Spanish merchant, to Cadiz, where I arrived safe with all my treasure ; for he suffered me to be at no expenses in his house ; and from Cadiz I soon got my passage on board an English merchant-ship for London, from whence I sent an account of my adventures to my wife, and where, in about five months more, she came over to me, leaving with full satisfaction the management of all our affairs in Virginia in the same faithful hands as before.

END OF THE LIFE OF COLONEL JACQUE.

# EVERYBODY'S BUSINESS IS

# NOBODY'S BUSINESS

# PREFACE

SINCE this little book appeared in print, it has had no less than three answers, and fresh attacks are daily expected from the powers of Grub Street; but should threescore antagonists more arise, unless they say more to the purpose than the fore-mentioned, they shall not tempt me to reply.

Nor shall I engage in a paper war, but leave my book to answer for itself, having advanced nothing therein but evident truths and incontestable matters of fact.

The general objection is against my style: I do not set up for an author, but write only to be understood, no matter how plain.

As my intentions are good, so have they had the good fortune to meet with approbation from the sober and substantial part of mankind; as for the vicious and vagabond, their ill-will is my ambition.

It is with uncommon satisfaction I see the magistracy begin to put the laws against vagabonds in force with the utmost vigour, a great many of those vermin, the japanners, having lately been taken up and sent to the several workhouses in and about this city; and indeed high time, for they grow every day more and more pernicious.

My project for putting watermen under commissioners will, I hope, be put in practice; for it is scarce safe to go by water unless you know your man.

As for the maid-servants, if I undervalue myself to take notice of them, as they are pleased to say, it is because they overvalue themselves so much they ought to be taken notice of.

This makes the guilty take my subject by the wrong end; but any impartial reader may find I write, not against servants, but bad servants; not against wages, but exorbitant wages, and am entirely of the poet's opinion—

> " The good should meet with favour and applause,
> The wicked be restrained by wholesome laws."

The reason why I did not publish this book till the end of the last sessions of Parliament was because I did not care to interfere with more momentous affairs, but leave it to the consideration of that august body during this recess, against the next sessions, when I shall exhibit another complaint against a growing abuse, for which I doubt not but to receive their approbation and the thanks of all honest men.

# EVERYBODY'S BUSINESS IS
# NOBODY'S BUSINESS

THIS is a proverb so common in everybody's mouth that I wonder nobody has yet thought it worth while to draw proper inferences from it, and expose those little abuses which, though they seem trifling, and as it were scarce worth consideration, yet, by insensible degrees, they may become of injurious consequence to the public; like some diseases, whose first symptoms are only trifling disorders, but by continuance and progression, their last periods terminate in the destruction of the whole human fabric.

In contradiction, therefore, to this general rule, and out of sincere love and well-meaning to the public, give me leave to enumerate the abuses insensibly crept in among us, and the inconveniences daily arising from the insolence and intrigues of our servant-wenches, who, by their caballing together, have made their party so considerable that everybody cries out against them; and yet, to verify the proverb, nobody has thought of, or at least proposed, a remedy, although such an undertaking, mean as it seems to be, I hope will one day be thought worthy the consideration of our king, Lords, and Commons.

Women-servants are now so scarce that, from thirty and forty shillings a year, their wages are increased of late to six, seven, nay, eight pounds per annum, and upwards, insomuch that an ordinary tradesman cannot well keep one; but his wife, who might be useful in his shop or business, must do the drudgery of household affairs; and all this because our servant-wenches are so puffed up with pride nowadays, that they never think they go fine enough. It is a hard matter to know the mistress from the maid by their dress; nay, very often the maid shall be much the finer of the two. Our woollen manufacture suffers much by this, for nothing but silks and satins will go down with our kitchen-wenches; to support which intolerable pride they have insensibly raised their wages to such a height as was never known in any age or nation but this.

Let us trace this from the beginning, and suppose a person has a servant-maid sent him out of the country, at fifty shillings or three pounds a year. The girl has scarce been a week, nay, a day, in her service but a committee of servant-wenches are appointed to examine her, who advise her to raise her wages or give warning; to encourage her to which, the herb-woman, or chandler-woman, or some other old intelligencer, provides her a place of four or five pounds a year. This sets madam cock-a-hoop, and she thinks of nothing now but vails and high wages, and so gives warning from place to place, till she has got her wages up to the tip-top.

Her neat's leathern shoes are now transformed into laced ones with light heels; her yarn stockings are turned into fine woollen ones, with silk clocks; and her high wooden pattens are kicked away for leathern clogs. She must have a hoop, too, as well as her mistress; and her poor scanty linsey-woolsey petticoat is changed into a good silk one, four or five yards wide at the least.

Not to carry the description further, in short, plain country Joan is now turned into a fine London madam, can drink tea, take snuff, and carry herself as high as the best.

If she be tolerably handsome and has any share of cunning, the apprentice or her master's son is enticed away and ruined by her. Thus many good families are impoverished and disgraced by those pert sluts, who, taking the advantage of a young man's simplicity and unruly desires, draw many heedless youths, nay, some of good estates, into their snares; and of this we have but too many instances.

Some more artful shall conceal their condition, and palm themselves off on young fellows for gentlewomen and great fortunes. How many families have been ruined by these ladies, when the father or master of the family, preferring the flirting airs of a young prinked-up strumpet to the artless sincerity of a plain, grave, and good wife, has given his desires a loose, and destroyed soul, body, family, and estate? But they are very favourable if they wheedle nobody into matrimony, but only make a present of a small live creature, no bigger than a bastard, to some of the family; no matter who gets it, when a child is born it must be kept.

Our sessions papers of late are crowded with instances of servant-maids robbing their places. This can be only attributed to their devilish pride, for their whole inquiry nowadays is, how little they shall do, how much they shall have.

But all this while they make so little reserve that if they fall sick the parish must keep them; if they are out of place they must prostitute their bodies, or starve; so that from chopping and changing, they generally proceed to whoring and thieving, and this is the reason why our streets swarm with strumpets.

Thus many of them rove from place to place, from

bawdy-house to service, and from service to bawdy-house again, ever unsettled and never easy, nothing being more common than to find these creatures one week in a good family, and the next in a brothel. This amphibious life makes them fit for neither; for if the bawd uses them ill, away they trip to service; and if the mistress gives them a wry word, whip they are at a bawdy-house again, so that in effect they neither make good whores nor good servants.

Those who are not thus slippery in the tail are light of finger; and of these the most pernicious are those who beggar you inchmeal. If a maid is a downright thief, she strips you at once, and you know your loss; but these retail pilferers waste you insensibly, and though you hardly miss it, yet your substance shall decay to such a degree that you must have a very good bottom indeed not to feel the ill effects of such moths in your family.

Tea, sugar, wine, &c., or any such trifling commodities, are reckoned no thefts; if they do not directly take your pewter from your shelf or your linen from your drawers, they are very honest. "What harm is there," say they, "in cribbing a little matter for a junket, a merry bout or so?" Nay, there are those that, when they are sent to market for one joint of meat, shall take up two on their master's account, and leave one by the way; for some of these maids are mighty charitable, and can make a shift to maintain a small family with what they can purloin from their masters and mistresses.

If you send them with ready money they turn factors, and take threepence or fourpence in the shilling brokerage. And here let me take notice of one very heinous abuse, not to say petty felony, which is practised in most of the great families about town, which is, when the tradesman gives the housekeeper or other commanding servant a penny or twopence in the shilling, or so much in the pound, for everything they send in, and which, from thence, is called poundage.

This, in my opinion, is the greatest of villainies, and ought to incur some punishment, yet nothing is more common, and our topping tradesmen, who seem otherwise to stand mightily on their credit, make this but a matter of course and custom. "If I do not," says one, "another will" (for the servant is sure to pick a hole in the person's coat who shall not pay contribution). Thus this wicked practice is carried on and winked at, while receiving of stolen goods and confederating with felons, which is not a jot worse, is so openly cried out against and severely punished; witness Jonathan Wild.

And yet, if a master or mistress inquire after anything missing, they must be sure to place their words in due form, or madam huffs and flings about at a strange rate. What! would you make a thief of her? Who would live with such mistrustful folks? Thus you are obliged to hold your tongue and sit down quietly by your loss, for fear of offending your maid, forsooth!

Again, if your maid shall maintain one, two, or more persons from your table, whether they are her poor relations, countryfolk, servants out of place, shoecleaners, charwomen, porters, or any other of her menial servants who do her ladyship's drudgery and go of her errands, you must not complain at your expense, or ask what has become of such a thing, or such a thing, although it might never so reasonably be supposed that it was altogether impossible to have so much expended in your family, but hold your tongue for peace' sake, or madam will say you grudge her victuals, and expose you to the last degree all over the neighbourhood.

Thus have they a salve for every sore, cheat you to

your face, and insult you into the bargain; nor can you help yourself without exposing yourself or putting yourself into a passion.

Another great abuse crept in among us is the giving of vails to servants. This was intended originally as an encouragement to such as were willing and handy; but by custom and corruption it is now grown to be a thorn in our sides, and, like other good things abused, does more harm than good, for now they make it a perquisite, a material part of their wages; nor must their master give a supper but the maid expects the guests should pay for it, nay, sometimes through the nose. Thus have they spirited people up to this unnecessary and burthensome piece of generosity unknown to our forefathers, who only gave gifts to servants at Christmastide—which custom is yet kept into the bargain; insomuch that a maid shall have eight pounds per annum in a gentleman's or merchant's family; and if her master is a man of free spirit, who receives much company, she very often doubles her wages by her vails. Thus, having meat, drink, washing, and lodging for her labour, she throws her whole income upon her back, and by this means looks more like the mistress of the family than the servant-wench.

And now we have mentioned washing, I would ask some good housewifely gentlewoman if servant-maids wearing printed linens, cottons, and other things of that nature, which require frequent washing, do not, by enhancing the article of soap, add more to housekeeping than the generality of people would imagine. And yet these wretches cry out against great washes, when their own unnecessary dabs are very often the occasion.

But the greatest abuse of all is, that these creatures are become their own lawgivers; nay, I think they are ours too, though nobody would imagine that such a set of slatterns should bamboozle a whole nation. But it is neither better nor worse; they hire themselves to you by their own rule;

That is, a month's wages, or a month's warning; if they don't like you, they will go away the next day, help yourself how you can. If you don't like them, you must give them a month's wages to get rid of them.

This custom of warning, as practised by our maid-servants, is now become a great inconvenience to masters and mistresses. You must carry your dish very upright, or miss, forsooth! gives you warning, and you are either left destitute, or to seek for a servant; so that, generally speaking, you are seldom or never fixed, but always at the mercy of every new-comer to divulge your family affairs, to inspect your private life, and treasure up the sayings of yourself and friends: a very great confinement, and much complained of in most families.

Thus have these wenches, by their continual plotting and cabals, united themselves into a formidable body, and got the whip-hand of their betters. They make their own terms with us; and two servants now will scarce undertake the work which one might perform with ease; notwithstanding which they have raised their wages to a most exorbitant pitch; and I doubt not, if there be not a stop put to their career, but they will bring wages up to £20 per annum in time, for they are much about half-way already.

It is by these means they run away with a great part of our money, which might be better employed in trade; and what is worse, by their insolent behaviour, their pride in dress, and their exorbitant wages, they give birth to the following inconveniences :—

First, They set an ill example to our children, our apprentices, our covenant servants, and other dependents, by their saucy and insolent behaviour, their pert and sometimes abusive answers, their daring defiance of correction, and many other insolences which youth are but too apt to imitate.

Secondly, By their extravagance in dress they put our wives and daughters upon yet greater excesses, because they will, as indeed they ought, go finer than the maid. Thus the maid striving to outdo the mistress, the tradesman's wife to outdo the gentleman's wife, the gentleman's wife emulating the lady, and the ladies one another, it seems as if the whole business of the female sex were nothing but an excess of pride and extravagance in dress.

Thirdly, The great height to which women-servants have brought their wages makes a mutiny among the men-servants, and puts them upon raising their wages too; so that in a little time our servants will become our partners; nay, probably, run away with the better part of our profits, and make servants of us *vice versâ*. But yet, with all these inconveniences, we cannot possibly do without these creatures; let us therefore cease to talk of the abuses arising from them, and begin to think of redressing them. I do not set up for a lawgiver, and therefore shall lay down no certain rules, humbly submitting in all things to the wisdom of our legislature. What I offer shall be under correction, and upon conjecture, my utmost ambition being but to give some hints to remedy this growing evil, and leave the prosecution to abler hands.

And first it would be necessary to settle and limit their wages from forty and fifty shillings to four and five pounds per annum—that is to say, according to their merits and capacities. For example, a young, inexperienced servant should have forty shillings per annum, till she qualifies herself for a larger sum; a servant who can do all household work, or, as the good women term it, can take her work and leave her work, should have four pounds per annum; and those who have lived seven years in one service should ever after demand five pounds per annum. For I would very fain have some particular encouragements and privileges given to such servants who should continue long in a place; it would incite a desire to please, and cause an emulation very beneficial to the public.

I have heard of an ancient charity in the parish of St Clement's Danes, where a sum of money or estate is left, out of the interest or income of which such maid-servants who have lived in that parish seven years in one service receive a reward of ten pounds apiece, if they please to demand it.

This is a noble benefaction, and shows the public spirit of the donor; but everybody's business is nobody's; nor have I heard that such reward has been paid to any servant of late years. A thousand pities a gift of that nature should sink into oblivion, and not be kept up as an example to incite all parishes to do the like.

The Romans had a law called *Jus Trium Liberorum*, by which every man who had been a father of three children had particular honours and privileges. This incited the youth to quit a dissolute single life and become fathers of families, to the support and glory of the Empire.

In imitation of this most excellent law, I would have such servants who should continue many years in one service meet with singular esteem and reward.

The apparel of our women-servants should be next regulated, that we may know the mistress from the maid. I remember I was once put very much to blush; being at a friend's house, and by him required to salute the ladies, I kissed the chamber-jade into the bargain, for she was as well dressed as the best. But I was soon undeceived by a general titter, which gave me the utmost confusion ; nor can I believe myself the only person who has made such a mistake.

Things of this nature would be easily avoided if servant-maids were to wear liveries, as our footmen do, or obliged to go in a dress suitable to their station. What should ail them but a jacket and petticoat of good yard-wide stuff or calimanco might keep them decent and warm ?

Our charity children are distinguished by their dress ; why, then, may not our women-servants ? Why may they not be made frugal perforce, and not suffered to put all on their backs, but obliged to save something against a rainy day ? I am therefore entirely against servants wearing of silks, laces, and other superfluous finery ; it sets them above themselves, and makes their mistresses contemptible in their eyes. " I am handsomer than my mistress," says a young prinked-up baggage; " what pity it is I should be her servant ! I go as well dressed, or better, than she." This makes the girl take the first offer to be made a whore, and there is a good servant spoiled ; whereas, were her dress suitable to her condition, it would teach her humility and put her in mind of her duty.

Besides, the fear of spoiling their clothes makes them afraid of household work ; so that in a little time we shall have none but chambermaids and nurserymaids ; and of this let me give one instance. My family is composed of myself and sister, a man and a maid ; and being without the last, a young wench came to hire herself. The man was gone out, and my sister above stairs, so I opened the door myself, and this person presented herself to my view, dressed completely, more like a visitor than a servant-maid. She, not knowing me, asked for my sister. " Pray, madam," said I, " be pleased to walk into the parlour ; she shall wait on you presently." Accordingly I handed madam in, who took it very cordially. After some apology I left her alone for a minute or two, while I, stupid wretch ! ran up to my sister and told her there was a gentlewoman below come to visit her. "Dear brother," said she, "don't leave her alone ; go down and entertain her while I dress myself." Accordingly down I went, and talked of indifferent affairs. Meanwhile my sister dressed herself all over again, not being willing to be seen in an undress. At last she came down dressed as clean as her visitor ; but how great was my surprise when I found my fine lady a common servant-wench !

My sister, understanding what she was, began to inquire what wages she expected. She modestly asked but eight pounds a year. The next question was, what work she could do to deserve such wages. To which she answered she could clean a house or dress a common family dinner. "But cannot you wash," replied my sister, "or get up linen ?" She answered in the negative, and said she would undertake neither, nor would she go into a family that did not put out their linen to wash and hire a charwoman to scour. She desired to see the house, and having carefully surveyed it, said the work was too hard for her, nor could she undertake it. This put my sister beyond all patience, and me into the greatest admiration. "Young woman," said she, "you have made a mistake ; I want a housemaid, and you are a chambermaid." "No, madam," replied she ; "I am not needlewoman enough for that." "And yet you ask eight pounds a year," replied my sister. "Yes, madam," said she ; "nor shall I bate a farthing." "Then get you gone for a lazy, impudent baggage," said I ; "you want to be a boarder, not a servant. Have you a fortune or estate that you dress at that rate ?" "No, sir," said she ; "but I hope I may wear what I work for without offence." "What you work !" interrupted my sister.

" Why, you do not seem willing to undertake any work.
You will not wash nor scour ; you cannot dress a dinner
for company ; you are no needlewoman ; and our little
house of two rooms on a floor is too much for you.
For God's sake, what can you do?" "Madam,"
replied she pertly, " I know my business, and do not
fear a service. There are more places than parish
churches. If you wash at home, you should have a
laundrymaid; if you give entertainments, you must
have a cookmaid ; if you have any needlework, you
should have a chambermaid ; and such a house as this
is enough for a housemaid in all conscience."

I was pleased at the wit and astonished at the impudence of the girl, so dismissed her with thanks for
her instructions, assuring her that when I kept four
maids she should be housemaid if she pleased.

Were a servant to do my business with cheerfulness,
I should not grudge at five or six pounds per annum ;
nor would I be so unchristian to put more upon any
one than they can bear ; but to pray and pay too is the
devil. It is very hard that I must keep four servants
or none.

In great families, indeed, where many servants are required, those distinctions of chambermaid, housemaid,
cookmaid, laundrymaid, nursery-maid, &c., are requisite,
to the end that each may take their particular business,
and many hands may make the work light ; but for a
private gentleman of a small fortune to be obliged to
keep so many idle jades, when one might do the business, is intolerable, and matter of great grievance.

I cannot close this discourse without a gentle ad-
monition and reproof to some of my own sex—I mean
those gentlemen who give themselves unnecessary airs,
and cannot go to see a friend but they must kiss and
slop the maid ; and all this is done with an air of
gallantry, and must not be resented. Nay, some gentle-

men are so silly that they shall carry on an under-hand affair with their friend's servant-maid, to their own disgrace and the ruin of many a young creature. Nothing is more base and ungenerous, yet nothing more common, and withal so little taken notice of. "D——n me, Jack," says one friend to another, "this maid of yours is a pretty girl; you do so and so to her, by G——d!" This makes the creature pert, vain, and impudent, and spoils many a good servant.

What gentleman will descend to this low way of intrigue, when he shall consider that he has a footboy or an apprentice for his rival, and that he is seldom or never admitted but when they have been his tasters? And the fool of fortune, though he comes at the latter end of the feast, yet pays the whole reckoning; and so indeed would I have all such silly cullies served.

If I must have an intrigue, let it be with a woman that shall not shame me. I would never go into the kitchen when the parlour door was open. We are forbidden at Highgate to kiss the maid when we may kiss the mistress. Why, then, will gentlemen descend so low, by too much familiarity with these creatures, to bring themselves into contempt?

I have been at places where the maid has been so dizzied with these idle compliments that she has mistook one thing for another, and not regarded her mistress in the least, but put on all the flirting airs imaginable. This behaviour is nowhere so much complained of as in taverns, coffee-houses, and places of public resort, where there are handsome bar-keepers, &c. These creatures, being puffed up with the fulsome flattery of a set of flesh-flies, which are continually buzzing about them, carry themselves with the utmost insolence imaginable, insomuch that you must speak to them with a great deal of deference, or you are sure to be affronted. Being at a coffee-house the other day, where one of these ladies kept the bar, I had bespoke a dish of rice tea ; but madam was so taken up with her sparks she had quite forgot it. I spake for it again, and with some temper, but was answered after a most taunting manner, not without a toss of the head, a contraction of the nostrils, and other impertinences too many to enumerate. Seeing myself thus publicly insulted by such an animal, I could not choose but show my resentment. "Woman," said I sternly, "I want a dish of rice tea, and not what your vanity and impudence may imagine ; therefore treat me as a gentleman and a customer, and serve me with what I call for. Keep your impertinent repartees and impudent behaviour for the coxcombs that swarm round your bar and make you so vain of your blown carcass." And indeed I believe the insolence of this creature will ruin her master at last, by driving away men of sobriety and business, and making the place a den of vagabonds and rakehells.

Gentlemen, therefore, ought to be very circumspect in their behaviour, and not undervalue themselves to servant-wenches, who are but too apt to treat a gentleman ill whenever he puts himself into their power.

Let me now beg pardon for this digression, and return to my subject by proposing some practicable methods for regulating of servants, which, whether they are followed or not, yet, if they afford matter of improvement and speculation, will answer the height of my expectation, and I will be the first who shall approve of whatever improvements are made from this small beginning.

The first abuse I would have reformed is, that servants should be restrained from throwing themselves out of place on every idle vagary. This might be remedied were all contracts between master and servant made before a justice of peace or other proper officer, and a memorandum thereof taken in writing. Nor should such servant leave his or her place (for men and maids might come under the same regulation) till the time agreed on be expired, unless such servant be misused or denied necessaries, or show some other reasonable cause for their discharge. In that case the master or mistress should be reprimanded or fined. But if servants misbehave themselves, or leave their places, not being regularly discharged, they ought to be amerced or punished. But all those idle, ridiculous customs and laws of their own making, as a month's wages or a month's warning, and such like, should be entirely set aside and abolished.

When a servant has served the limited time duly and faithfully, they should be entitled to a certificate, as is practised at present in the wool-combing trade ; nor should any person hire a servant without a certificate or other proper security. A servant without a certificate should be deemed a vagrant ; and a master or mistress ought to assign very good reasons indeed when they object against giving a servant his or her certificate.

And though, to avoid prolixity, I have not mentioned footmen particularly in the foregoing discourse, yet the complaints alleged against the maids are as well masculine as feminine, and very applicable to our gentlemen's gentlemen. I would, therefore, have them under the very same regulations, and, as they are fellow-servants, would not make fish of one and flesh of the other, since daily experience teaches us that "never a barrel the better herring."

The next great abuse among us is, that under the notion of cleaning our shoes, above ten thousand wicked, idle, pilfering vagrants are permitted to patrol about our city and suburbs. These are called the black-guard, who black your honour's shoes, and incorporate themselves under the title of the Worshipful Company of Japanners.

Were this all, there were no hurt in it, and the whole might terminate in a jest; but the mischief ends not here: they corrupt our youth, especially our men-servants; oaths and impudence are their only flowers of rhetoric; gaming and thieving are the principal parts of their profession; japanning but the pretence. For example, a gentleman keeps a servant, who, among other things, is to clean his master's shoes; but our gentlemen's gentlemen are above it nowadays, and your man's man performs the office, for which piece of service you pay double and treble, especially if you keep a table—nay, you are well off if the japanner has no more than his own diet from it.

I have often observed these rascals sneaking from gentlemen's doors with wallets or hats full of good victuals, which they either carry to their trulls or sell for a trifle. By this means our butcher's, our baker's, our poulterer's, and cheesemonger's bills are monstrously exaggerated; not to mention candles just lighted, which sell for fivepence a pound, and many other perquisites best known to themselves and the pilfering villains their confederates.

Add to this that their continual gaming sets servants upon their wits to supply this extravagance, though at the same time the master's pocket pays for it, and the time which should be spent in a gentleman's service is loitered away among these rakehells, insomuch that half our messages are ineffectual, the time intended being often expired before the message is delivered.

How many frequent robberies are committed by these japanners? And to how many more are they confederates? Silver spoons, spurs, and other small pieces of plate are every day missing, and very often found upon these sort of gentlemen; yet are they permitted, to the shame of all our good laws and the scandal of our most excellent government, to lurk about our streets, to debauch our servants and apprentices, and support an infinite number of scandalous, shameless trulls, yet more wicked than themselves—for not a Jack among them but must have his Gill.

By whom such indecencies are daily acted, even in our open streets, as are very offensive to the eyes and ears of all sober persons, and even abominable in a Christian country.

In any riot or other disturbance these sparks are always the foremost; for most among them can turn their hands to picking of pockets, to run away with goods from a fire, or other public confusion, to snatch anything from a woman or child, to strip a house when the door is open, or any other branch of a thief's profession.

In short, it is a nursery for thieves and villains; modest women are every day insulted by them and their strumpets; and such children who run about the streets, or those servants who go on errands, do but too frequently bring home some scraps of their beastly profane wit; insomuch that the conversation of our lower rank of people runs only upon bawdy and blasphemy, notwithstanding our societies for reformation and our laws in force against profaneness. For this lazy life gets them many proselytes, their numbers daily increasing from runaway apprentices and footboys, insomuch that it is a very hard matter for a gentleman to get him a servant or for a tradesman to find an apprentice.

Innumerable other mischiefs accrue, and others will spring up from this race of caterpillars, who must be swept from out our streets, or we shall be overrun with all manner of wickedness.

But the subject is so low, it becomes disagreeable even to myself; give me leave, therefore, to propose a way to clear the streets of these vermin, and to substitute as many honest, industrious persons in their stead, who are now starving for want of bread, while these execrable villains live, though in rags and nastiness, yet in plenty and luxury.

I therefore humbly propose that these vagabonds be put immediately under the command of such taskmasters as the government shall appoint, and that they be employed, punished, or rewarded, according to their capacities and demerits ; that is to say, the industrious and docible to wool-combing, and other parts of the woollen manufacture, where hands are wanted, as also to husbandry and other parts of agriculture.

For it is evident that there are scarce hands enow in the country to carry on either of these affairs. Now these vagabonds might not only by this means be kept out of harm's way, but be rendered serviceable to the nation. Nor is there any need of transporting them beyond seas ; for if any are refractory, they should be sent to our stanneries and other mines, to our coal-works and other places where hard labour is required. And here I must offer one thing never yet thought of or proposed by any, and that is, the keeping in due repair the navigation of the river Thames, so useful to our trade in general ; and yet of late years such vast hills of sand are gathered together in several parts of the river as are very prejudicial to its navigation, one which is near London Bridge, another near Whitehall, a third near Battersea, and a fourth near Fulham. These are of very great hindrance to the navigation ; and indeed the removal of them ought to be a national concern, which I humbly propose may be thus effected.

The rebellious part of these vagabonds, as also other thieves and offenders, should be formed into bodies under the command of proper officers, and under the guard and awe of our soldiery. These should every day at low water carry away these sandhills, and remove every other obstruction to the navigation of this most excellent and useful river.

It may be objected that the ballast-men might do this; that as fast as the hills are taken away they would gather together again; or that the watermen might do it. To the first I answer, that ballast-men, instead of taking away from these hills, make holes in other places of the river, which is the reason so many young persons are drowned when swimming or bathing in the river.

Besides, it is a work for many hands and of long continuance; so that ballast-men do more harm than good. The second objection is as silly; as if I should never wash myself because I shall be dirty again, and, I think, needs no other answer. And as to the third objection, the watermen are not so public-spirited; they live only from hand to mouth, though not one of them but finds the inconvenience of these hills, every day being obliged to go a great way round about for fear of running aground; insomuch that in a few years the navigation of that part of the river will be entirely obstructed. Nevertheless, every one of these gentlemen-watermen hopes it will last his time, and so they all cry, "The devil take the hindmost." But yet I judge it highly necessary that this be made a national concern, like Dagenham breach, and that these hills be removed by some means or other.

And now I have mentioned watermen, give me leave to complain of the insolences and exactions they daily commit on the river Thames, and in particular this one instance, which cries aloud for justice.

A young lady of distinction, in company with her brother, a little youth, took a pair of oars at or near the Temple on April day last, and ordered the men to carry them to Pepper Alley Stairs. One of the fellows, according to their usual impertinence, asked the lady where she was going. She answered, near St Olave's

Church. Upon which he said she had better go through the bridge. The lady replied she had never gone through the bridge in her life, nor would she venture for a hundred guineas; so commanded him once more to land her at Pepper Alley Stairs. Notwithstanding which, in spite of her fears, threats, and commands—nay, in spite of the persuasion of his fellow, he forced her through London Bridge, which frightened her beyond expression. And, to mend the matter, he obliged her to pay double fare, and mobbed her into the bargain.

To resent which abuse, application was made to the Hall, the fellow summoned, and the lady ordered to attend, which she did, waiting there all the morning, and was appointed to call again in the afternoon. She came accordingly. They told her the fellow had been there, but was gone, and that she must attend another Friday. She attended again and again, but to the same purpose. Nor have they yet produced the man, but tired out the lady, who has spent above ten shillings in coach-hire, been abused and baffled into the bargain.

It is pity, therefore, there are not commissioners for watermen, as there are for hackney-coachmen, or that justices of the peace might not inflict bodily penalties on watermen thus offending. But while watermen are watermen's judges, I shall laugh at those who carry their complaints to the Hall.

The usual plea in behalf of abusive watermen is, that they are drunk, ignorant, or poor; but will that satisfy the party aggrieved, or deter the offender from re-offending? Whereas were the offender sent to the House of Correction, and there punished, or sentenced to work at the sandhills afore mentioned for a time suitable to the nature of their crimes, terror of such punishments would make them fearful of offending, to the great quiet of the subject.

Now, it may be asked, "How shall we have our shoes cleaned, or how are those industrious poor to be maintained?" To this I answer that the places of these vagabonds may be very well supplied by great numbers of ancient persons, poor widows, and others, who have not enough from their respective parishes to maintain them. These poor people I would have authorised and stationed by the justices of the peace or other magistrates. Each of these should have a particular walk or stand, and no other shoe-cleaner should come into that walk, unless the person misbehave and be removed. Nor should any person clean shoes in the streets but these authorised shoe-cleaners, who should have some mark of distinction, and be under the immediate government of the justices of the peace.

Thus would many thousands of poor people be provided for without burthening their parishes. Some of these may earn a shilling or two in a day, and none less than sixpence, or thereabouts.

And, lest the old japanners should appear again, in the shape of linkboys, and knock down gentlemen in drink, or lead others out of the way into dark, remote places, where they either put out their lights and rob them themselves, or run away and leave them to be pillaged by others, as is daily practised, I would have no person carry a link for hire but some of these industrious poor, and even such not without some ticket or badge to let people know whom they trust. Thus would the streets be cleared night and day of these vermin; nor would oaths, skirmishes, blasphemy, obscene talk, or other wicked examples be so public and frequent. All gaming at orange and gingerbread barrows should be abolished, as also all penny and halfpenny lotteries, thimbles, and balls, &c., so frequent in Moorfields, Lincoln's Inn Fields, &c., where idle fellows resort to play with children and apprentices, and tempt them to steal their parents' or masters' money.

There is one admirable custom in the city of London which I could wish were imitated in the city and liberties of Westminster, and bills of mortality, which is, no porter can carry a burthen or letter in the City unless he be a ticket-porter; whereas, out of the freedom part of London, any person may take a knot and turn porter, till he be entrusted with something of value, and then you never hear of him more.

This is very common, and ought to be amended. I would, therefore, have all porters under some such regulation as coachmen, chairmen, carmen, &c.; a man may then know whom he entrusts, and not run the risk of losing his goods, &c. Nay, I would not have a person carry a basket in the markets who is not subject to some regulation; for very many persons oftentimes lose their dinners in sending their meat home by persons they know nothing of.

Thus would all our poor be stationed; and a man or woman able to perform any of these offices must either comply or be termed an idle vagrant, and sent to a place where they shall be forced to work. By this means industry will be encouraged, idleness punished, and we shall be famed, as well as happy, for our tranquillity and decorum.

# THE PROTESTANT MONASTERY

# PREFACE

A COMMONWEALTH is a machine actuated by many wheels, one dependent on the other, yet the obstruction of a small wheel may stop the motion of the whole. Every man ought, therefore, as much as in him lies, to contribute in his station to the public welfare, and not be afraid or ashamed of doing, or at least meaning, well.

I hope, therefore, the reader will excuse the vanity of an over-officious old man if, like Cato, I inquire whether or no, before I go hence, and be no more, I can yet do anything for the service of my country.

For if every man should say, "Children are burthensome and the cause of many sorrows, therefore will not I be a father," farewell to all ties of nature and every blessing of human society.

Or if every man should say to himself, "What have I to do with State affairs? Is it my business? Are there not enough at the helm? What need I interfere? Let me be subject to the higher powers, and, let matters sink or swim, I shall have neighbours' fare."

Would not this be a very churlish resolution? Would it not very much contribute to universal anarchy and confusion? Should every man thus throw the care of the public from his shoulders, and acquit himself of any concern for the rest of mankind?

This would be my case should I, knowing I am master of a project which in all probability may be of great use to mankind, reason thus to myself: " What have I to do to divulge my secrets? What though they are of benefit to the public? shall I reap any advantage by them? Shall I not rather be laughed at and despised as a projector, the most contemptible character in this part of the world? May not another run away with the profits of my labour, and by a little improvement make my project his own? Is it not better for me to repose myself, to die in peace, and leave an ungrateful world to their own imaginations?" *Non nobis nati sumus.* That thought would quash all harsh contemplations. I could hazard with pleasure the public contumely for the public good, knowing it has been the fate of much better men than myself to be despised when living though revered when dead.

Prompted by this reflection, I once more take pen in hand, as I hope, for the service of my country. If my countrymen find what I advance practicable, I hope they will not call my integrity in question; and if they have patience to read my well-intended thoughts, though digested, I fear, but too mildly and in too mean a style, I hope they will find I have advanced nothing but what is practicable, beneficial, and without self-interest, having excluded myself from any propriety in my own project by thus publishing it and making it everybody's; and if any think I write for money, let them ask my bookseller.

Alas! I have but small health and little leisure to turn author, being now in my sixty-seventh year, almost worn out with age and sickness. The old man cannot trouble you long; take, then, in good part his best intentions, and impute his defects to age and weakness.

Look on him as a man of more experience than learning; excuse his style for the sake of his subject, and take the will for the deed. Assure yourself, gentle reader, I had not published my project in this pamphlet could I have got it inserted in any of the journals without feeing the journalists or publishers.

I cannot but have the vanity to think they might as well have inserted what I sent them (gratis) as many things I have since seen in their papers. But I have not only had the mortification to find what I sent rejected, but to lose my originals, not having taken copies of what I wrote.

However, to justify my complaints to the world, I shall, in a proper place, let them know the substance of what was rejected, and by whom.

In the meantime give me leave to assure my readers that the reason why this project appears in a pamphlet is because I have been thus baffled and disheartened by journalists; for if, by any means, the public could have had it at a cheaper rate, I had been better pleased.

# THE PROTESTANT MONASTERY

THERE is nothing on earth more shocking, and withal more common, in but too many families, than to see age and grey hairs derided and ill-used. The old man or the old woman can do nothing to please; their words are perverted, their actions misrepresented, and themselves looked upon as a burthen to their issue, and a rent-charge upon those who came from their loins.

This treatment, as it is directly opposite to the dignity and decency of human nature, calls aloud for redress; the helpless and innocent ought to be the care of the healthy and able. Shall a man or woman toil and moil to bring up a numerous issue? Shall they rear up, through all the uncertainties and fatigues of childhood, a race who shall spring up but to abandon them? Shall they enfeeble themselves to give strength to those who shall one day thrust them aside and despise them?

Yet this is the case of many aged persons who have outlived the comforts of this world; who survive only to hear themselves wished out of the way by those very persons upon whom they have bestowed their whole substance, and upon whom their whole hopes have been fixed. Uncertain hopes indeed, and far unfit for so degenerate an age! " Honour thy father and thy mother" is a commandment given by God, and ratified by our Blessed Saviour both in precept and example; if so, what brutes are those who shall dare to spurn those persons whom God has thought fit to make the means of their entrance into human life!

But, indeed, not only parents, but all aged people in general are thought to stand in the way of the present generation; and but for some good children, some persons of tenderness and humanity, who honour the hoary head and comfort the feeble, immediate vengeance would be pulled down on those who let not their sires live out half their days.

The word "old" is a standing jest among our youthful gentry. When they would frighten children, they tell them "the old man's a-coming." Thus they inculcate an abhorrence of age, even in sucking babes, which no doubt will improve with adult age, according to the proverb:—

> " Quo semel est imbuta recens, servabit odorem
>    Testa diu."

If any whimsical or ridiculous story is told, 'tis of an old woman. If any person is awkward at his business or anything else, he is called an old woman, forsooth! But this is no new thing, for we read in former ages that they made witches of their old women. Those were brave days for young people, when they could swear the old ones out of their lives, and get a woman hanged or burnt only for being a little too old, as has been the case of many a poor innocent ancient creature. The story of the witch, *alias* the poor old woman of Hertford, is yet fresh in every one's memory; and had not the very judges on the bench seen through the enthusiasm and obstinacy of the evidence, who swore through thick and thin— had not the judges themselves, I say, represented the thing in a right light to the higher powers, poor Jane Wenman had certainly been trussed up, as a warning to all ancient persons who should dare to live longer than the young ones think convenient.

It is well it has never been in the young ones' power to bring in a Bill for the better trimming of mankind, *i.e.*, to knock all ancient people on the head.

But though they are suffered to live, 'tis under many hardships and restrictions, many humps and grumps, and scarce a day but they are asked what they do out of their graves. This is a very common, but withal a most impious and unchristian saying—nay, not only unchristian, but even unmahometan; for the very infidels themselves pay more veneration to old age than the Christians do, to the shame and scandal of our holy profession.

Far be it from me to tax all Christians or all children with so severe a reproach. No; I only blame those who triumph in the strength of their youth and snuff up their nostrils at old age; who laugh at the groanings of the hoary head, and have no bowels of compassion for the bowels that gave them nourishment.

Let such self-sufficient persons consider that it was once in their parents' power to have abandoned them, when they were more helpless than any other being to which God has given life, when they must inevitably have perished without great care and tenderness; and indeed the Divine Wisdom is most manifestly seen in making man the chief of all His earthly creatures, to require so delicate a management and so tender a nourishment; parental love being increased by its care, as filial love ought to be, by a gratitude for that care it can never too much acknowledge or repay.

All creatures whom God has ordained to quit their sires, or indeed those whom He has not endowed with a rational soul to distinguish between good and bad, or to know duty or obligation, are easily brought up, and can help themselves better the hour they are born than man can in a whole year—nay, in years. They perform all the necessary functions of life, and there is no need of education. Far otherwise is it with man; he in his infancy requires a constant and careful attendance, his members know not their functions, and it is a long while before he can feed himself. Even then his parents have the care for his food. When the body is duly nourished, there is yet a further care to form the mind and cultivate the rational soul God has endowed him with.

Shall such a being, possessed of a rational soul to distinguish between good and bad, between gratitude and ingratitude, so far debase himself, or indeed become so much a brute, as to forsake his parent, to spurn him who begot him; or at least, by using him ill, to allow him, as it were, out of the world, to give himself the greater scope for luxury?

Yet how many do we see of such! How many truly compassionate hearts daily bleed when they see the son curbing the father or the daughter snubbing the mother! It seems as if the order of nature were perverted, so shocking is it to any soul who has the least tincture of humanity.

I am sure I speak by experience, for but very lately I went to see an old schoolfellow and acquaintance of mine who had lately married his daughter, and settled himself in her family; accordingly he gave me a general invitation to come one day or other and take a dinner with him. He had been a merchant from his youth, and always lived in what we call high life, had travelled much, and was master of the most good manners I ever met with.

This gentleman, being very weary, and indeed almost incapable of business, thought it best to leave off housekeeping, to marry his daughter, and settle in her family. Accordingly he gave her his all for her portion, made her a fortune of £12,000, and matched her to an eminent merchant who used the same trade with himself.

During the honeymoon, and till the portion was paid, the old gentleman lived in clover ; nothing was too hot or too heavy for him. 'Twas "Dear sir ! " "Dear father ! " at every word ; the servants were ordered to respect him, and he was in some share master of the family. But, alas ! he found this but a short-lived dream ; the servants began to taunt at him, and he must call twenty times for a thing before he could have it. If he gently chid them or reasoned with them, they flew to their mistress and made twenty stories about it, so that his life was, in a manner, a burthen to him.

I went in my chariot to see him, and had not the little appearance I made commanded some respect, I had danced attendance till they should find in their hearts to call him. However, without much ceremony, they directed me up three pair of stairs into a better sort of a garret ; there might be, indeed, some lodging-rooms overhead for the servants, but I have seen many servants have much better apartments. But the room would not have so much surprised me had the furniture been anything tolerable. I dare swear it was as old as the house, and had no doubt passed from tenant to tenant half a score times.

This I thought an odd residence for my friend, but he seemed contented, and I saw no reason I had to make him otherwise. He amused me till dinner-time with showing me his books and reading some of his verses to me, he having a pretty knack that way. He would have played me a lesson on his flute but that he said it would disturb his daughter, who did not love music. I saw that all his little arts were only to

beguile the time, lest a whet before dinner, which I
never missed at his house, should be expected, and
which, I believe, was now out of his power to give.
At last the bell rang, and he desired me to walk down
to dinner, but with an air that seemed chidingly to
say, "Ah! why did you not come sooner, when I had
more authority?" However, with a long apology to his
son and daughter, he introduced me, and by pleading
our long and intimate acquaintance and the obligations
he was under to me, he prevailed on them at last to
bid me a very ceremonious welcome. Excusing themselves, as indeed they had need, that they had not
made a proper provision, and pleading their ignorance
of my coming, accordingly down we sat to some cold
roast-beef, a few herrings, and a plate of fritters. Everything was indeed very clean, and we had attendance
enough, but never in my life made I a worse dinner.
Herrings are my aversion; I never eat cold meat.
Judge, then, what a bellyful I could make of my share
of the fritters. I happened by mistake to call for a
glass of wine, without which I never dine, when the
gentleman told me he had none in the house, but if I
pleased he would send for some, recommending at
the same time some of his home-brewed ale, which
I, in complaisance, could not but accept in preference
to wine. They took me at my word, and with much
ado I got down half a glass of the worst potion I ever
took in my life. But had the dinner been ever so ele-
gant, my indignation would have spoiled my stomach; to
hear the daughter at every turn take up her father in
his discourse, as if he had been an idiot or an underling,
with, "Oh, fie, sir!" and, "I wonder, father, you should
say so!" But lest the readers, by my recital of the
lady's phrases, should think my friend spake ludicrously
or indecently, I beg leave to assure them the contrary,
and that he is a man of great wit and strict modesty.

Even the son, who was the least severe upon him, could
not refrain from contradicting him every now and then,
merely for contradiction's sake, with "Pray, sir, give
me leave," and, "Indeed, sir, you have forgot yourself." This was my whole entertainment. For my
part, I said little, but admired not only at this wondrous
frugality, but the surprising impertinence and ingratitude
of the young couple. However, I was undeceived at
last, as I hope my readers will be when I assure them
that the reason why sir and madam ate so sparingly
with us was, because they had devoured in hugger-
mugger by themselves a good handsome fowl and
oyster sauce, and dispensed with a bottle of wine,
though they could drink none in our company.

Seeing this penurious management and the awe my
poor friend was in, I thought it best to adjourn to the
tavern to smoke a pipe, and withal to take a glass to
warm my stomach, which raked prodigiously. I had
before learned that the poor old soul had been obliged
to leave off smoking, because, forsooth! his spitting and
spawling turned madam's stomach. His smoking, she
said, made the house stink and damaged the furniture.
He had been from his youth a great smoker, and this
sudden check upon a habit of so long standing had
very much impaired his health.

Accordingly, to the tavern we went, where a pipe
and a bottle gave new life to my old acquaintance.
He resumed his native gaiety, and eleven of the clock
stole upon us before we could think of parting, and
even then but with great reluctance, so agreeably did
the time pass away in recounting our old adventures.
Indeed our sweet was intermixed with sour, for his
poor heart was so full he could not contain himself
from lodging his sorrows in the bosom of his old
friend. With tears in his eyes he recounted all the
indignities he daily met with, not only from his own

children, but from the very servants. If he spake to
them as to servants, his daughter would take him up
and tell him he domineered too much in her house.
If he spake submissively, he was told he had no
occasion to make himself so little ; insomuch that he
knew not what medium to take.

He told me his daughter had lately a chambermaid
who was the daughter of a decayed gentleman, and
who, having had a tolerable education, had imbibed
high notions of virtue, and, amongst other things, an
abhorrence of undutifulness in children, or indeed any
disrespect in old age. This young woman, having
learned in what fashion my friend had once lived,
could not without indignation see how ill he was
treated, and being of a good family herself, scorned
to take part with the other servants to torment a poor
old man, but, on the contrary, would do him all the
Christian offices she could ; would constantly get him
something warm in a morning, and if he was out of
order at any time, would tend him, and do him a
thousand little services, for which he in recompense,
when her lady was gone a-visiting, would read to the
girl a whole afternoon together while she sat at work.
And as so many good offices must consequently engage her to him, especially when everybody else had
abandoned him, he, with an innocent familiarity,
used to call her his Nanny. This was taken in great
dudgeon, and the spiteful servants improved it into
an intrigue, and never left till poor Nanny was turned
away ; and with her all the old man's comfort, for he
had no warm breakfast now ; if he was sick, there he
might lie, for nobody would help him ; and as for
attendance, they neglected him so much he was scarce
clean, which drew tears from my eyes, as knowing what
a neat old man he used to be. And but for disgracing
his children, he wished himself a thousand times in the

Charterhouse, or some other place of public charity. I dissuaded him from such thoughts, and comforted him in the best manner I could ; and so we both parted, and ended our pleasant evening, with heavy hearts and wet eyes.

About a week after, by the penny-post, I received the following letter :—

" DEAR FRIEND,—Though I shall carry to my grave the agreeable remembrance of our last meeting, I believe I shall suffer to my dying day for that night's pleasure. Your engaging company and my long abstinence from wine made me, I think, drink a little too much ; and though not to disguise myself, as you, I hope, might well perceive, yet more than my age and weakness could well bear. My daughter, who seldom or never comes home before midnight, took care to be at home that very night before nine o'clock ; and at ten she sent all the family to bed and sat up for me herself, out of mere spite and pure intention to rattle me off, which she did with a vengeance, crying out shame of such hours, telling me I was drunk ; and when I complained of sickness at my stomach, she said it was good enough for me. This, you may conclude, made me worse. I thought I should have died, and had not I eased my stomach I had not survived that moment. This put her beyond all patience, and instead of pitying her almost dying father, she called me (would you believe it ?)—she called me ' old beast,' and used me in such a manner as has rived my very heart. Nor is this all, for ever since I am become the jest of the whole family. They call me ' old fool ' and ' drunken old beast ' to my face, and every visitor that comes in is told what a sot I am ; so that I keep my chamber and dare not show my head about the house. But I thank God, who has heard my prayers, that I hourly find myself weaker and weaker, and I doubt not but my long-wished-for dissolution is near at hand; for all the torments of a lingering death are trifles to the usage I meet with. Dear friend, let me see you once more before I die, having some manuscripts and a few other trifles to give you in remembrance of our old friendship; which, alas! is all I can give to the only friend I have left on this side the grave.——Your affectionate friend,

————,"

For the sake of the young lady, to whom God grant a speedy repentance, I forbear subscribing even the initial letters of her father's name, that the world may not know how good a man she has murdered; for her usage was such that, before I could find opportunity to visit him according to his desire, I was prevented by a ticket, which invited me to hold up his pall, which more surprised than afflicted me, as knowing the miserable life he had led under his most unnatural daughter:——

" Quis talia fando temperet a lachrymis?"

The burying was of a piece with the rest; and I hope the whole will be a warning to all aged persons, and teach them to reserve at least wherewithal to maintain themselves elsewhere, in case of the like usage from their children or relations.

I hope, at the same time, it will be a looking-glass to young people, especially those guilty of the like actions. If they see anything ugly in this lady's character, let them not be so over good-natured to their own persons as to think what is a crime in her may be excusable in themselves. No; the sin is the same, let who will commit it.

To do as we would be done by, one would think a sufficient restraint upon any who would give themselves the least time to consider that they in all probability may be fathers and mothers ; and that though they are young and healthy now, they may be old and feeble hereafter. Let them therefore use the old as they could wish to be used when they are so, and let them be as tender of their parents as they would have their posterity tender of them.

But, on the contrary, we bring up our youth, as it were, to despise us, and, to our shame be it spoken, make rods for ourselves. Every one indulges his own children, and so all act with impunity. Our youth are not half educated, nor are they under any restraint. We make men and women of them too soon, and put them upon a footing with ourselves before they have well learned good manners, or indeed anything else.

For good manners does not altogether consist in a formal courtesy or bow in coming in and going out of a room. No ; a man may behave himself most punctually ceremonious at a ball, a drawing-room, a tea-table, or indeed in any other fiddle-faddle part of life, and yet for all this be but a man of clouts— a mere Sir Courtly Nice. I have very often seen some of these well-dressed, well-bred gentlemen, *alias* Hobbydehoys, have assurance enough to stare a whole coffee-room out of countenance, but neither sense or learning sufficient to give any man of parts a reasonable answer.

No ; the satchel is too soon taken from the shoulders of our young sparks, and the rod from their backsides. The tie-wig and sword are too soon put on, and little master is made a man before he is a well-grown child. Our little girls, through the indulgence of their mothers, are yet more forward, and put on womanly airs even at ten years of age. In a word, our youth in general are above correction ; without shame, too ripe, too ignorant, and too impudent, and, according to the poet :—

> " Now little miss in hanging-sleeves knows more
> Than formerly her grandame at threescore :
> And master, who was lately whipped at school,
> At bare thirteen sets up for rake and fool,
> Runs the whole race of vice with full career,
> Is green, and ripe, and rotten in a year."

Instead of puerile diversions, our boys of fourteen or fifteen years of age go to plays, become members of clubs, keep hounds and horses, and sometimes follow worse game. This is owing to the over-indulgence of parents, who let them finger money before they know the worth of it ; and if a stop be not put to such practices in this generation, the next may severely repent it.

Instead of babies, play-things, and other pretty innocences used of old, our girls at ten or eleven years of age keep their visiting days, have their select companies, and treat them with as much solemnity and expense as their parents do their own acquaintance. This prevails not only at court, but in the City ; and I doubt not but the court airs of the mother and the womanly airs of the daughter have made bankrupt many an honest man, who had not courage enough to repel the force of this most prevailing, most pernicious custom.

This idle custom is not only very expensive, but extremely inconvenient withal ; for there is as much a fuss made at some houses against such a miss or such a miss comes to visit the daughter as if a duchess was expected. The servants are hindered from their other business, and the whole house is in a flutter to receive miss's visitors, forsooth ! When the visit is returned, she must be dressed up to the height of the mode, and some new thing or other is always wanted ; not to mention top-knots, gloves, coach-hire, and other unavoidable expenses.

This is most criminal in those who cannot afford it.

Such people would therefore do well to reduce their children to the old standard—that is to say, make scholars of their boys and housewives of their girls; for the education above complained of has spoiled many a good tradesman's wife and been the ruin of many a family.

I cannot close this discourse without particularly cautioning the young ladies of this age how they laugh, fleer, and toss up their noses at sober matrons and elderly ladies. Let them consider that those very persons were once young and beautiful as themselves, if not more beautiful; for, to say truth, tea, drams, wine, and late hours have not a jot added to the beauty of the present generation.

Let them, again, consider that their own mothers as well as themselves are of the same sex; that it is a foul bird bewrays its own nest; that the very infirmities they deride in those persons are probably occasioned by the bearing and bringing up many children; and that the wrinkles in their faces are occasioned by their care to support such giddy-brained creatures as themselves.

But such is the ignorance and impudence of the present generation that young people look upon their elders as upon a different species, an inferior class of people; they ascribe no merit to the virtue and experience of old age, but assume to themselves the preference in all things. With them a face and a good shape is merit, a scornful toss of the head and despising everybody but their own dear selves is wit, an everlasting giddiness and an eternal grin is affability and good nature, fancy in dress is understanding, a supine neglect of everything commendable gentility, and a prodigious punctilio in the greatest trifles is the height of good breeding.

From this general corruption in education proceeds

all that may be complained of in this present age, and
whatever evils may be expected in generations to come.
But, above all, nothing has more contributed to this
corruption than the disregard paid to teachers and
other persons concerned in the education of youth ;
for the first and chief step to the ruin of youth is
when they have no awe upon them and are above
correction.

" Spare the rod and spoil the child " is a sentence of
so much weight and truth that no sharper a reprimand
can be given to those parents who have stimulated in
their children a spirit of pride and taught them to
look contemptibly on their tutors.   The very word
"master" or "mistress" implies something of dominion,
and as youth are committed to their care, so they ought
to be subject to their discipline.

It shocks me when I see a tutor in a great family
put upon a footing with the servants.   It makes his
pupil think contemptibly of him, and is too great a
curb on his spirits to let him deliver his instructions
and sentiments in a manner suitable to the dignity of
an instructor.   And, what is worse, the little deference
paid to him begets in the young gentleman a mean
opinion of and indifference to learning itself, seeing his
master reap so little advantage and respect from it.

It is the same case in schools, where the master's
or mistress's passive and sordid temper makes them
the slaves of the scholars, whom they dare not correct
for fear of losing ; nothing being more common nowadays than for parents to make it in their bargain
that their children shall not be whipped or otherwise
corrected at school.   Hence proceeds all that noise
and misrule which reigns in schools, stunning both
master and scholars to such a degree that they can
hardly hear each other speak.

Parents therefore can blame none but themselves

if by these pernicious methods their children grow in time to be too many for them; nor can they with any reason expect to find duty and humanity where they have not been inculcated. If they have countenanced or indulged their children in deriding the hoary head, are they to be pitied when they reap sevenfold the fruits of so ungenerous a tillage? or, to speak more plain, when it comes home to themselves? Let every person, therefore, make the case their own when they see children taunting and flouncing at their parents, teachers, or relations; mocking and deriding people for age and infirmities, or indeed any other bodily misfortune or deformity; upbraiding any for their poverty, or crowing over any person over whom they may pretend to claim pre-eminence; this domineering way being nowadays so prevalent that tradesmen, servants, and other dependents are generally more insulted by children than by masters and mistresses themselves.

To conclude, as we sow we shall reap; as we bring up our children, so we may expect to find them. If we educate them in the nurture and fear of the Lord, in an universal benevolence to all mankind, void of all personal or party prejudice; if we train them up to be dutiful to their parents, respectful to their teachers, mannerly to their equals, and courteous to their inferiors; if we incite in them an emulation and thirst after knowledge and other liberal acquirements; if we instil into them early principles of humanity, compassion, and forbearance, and, in a word, all that may inspire to the highest notions of honour and carry human nature to its most exalted pitch, then may we expect to have comfort in old age, from our grandchildren, our children, and other relations; then may we conclude we have laid a sure foundation for the happiness of succeeding generations.

But if, on the contrary, we humour and favour all their little petulances, and by over-praising and indulging them make ourselves contemptible in their eyes; if, instead of correcting them in their errors, we arraign the justice of discipline and call it severity; if we suffer them with impunity to fly in the faces of their parents and relations, to defy their teachers, to outvie their equals, and insult their inferiors; if we permit them to scoff at and turn to ridicule the misfortunes and afflictions of others, and, in a manner, suppress, or at least not encourage, in them any propensity to tenderness, but suffer their hearts to be hardened and to know no pity, we must expect to have our eyes plucked out by those we have brought up. We must look for nothing in old age but contempt, oppression, and all the insults we have but too much reason to fear from so inhuman a generation.

# A PROJECT FOR ERECTING A PRO-TESTANT MONASTERY

1. THAT a joint-stock of twenty thousand pounds be raised between fifty persons, by an equal deposit of four hundred pounds each, which stock is to be vested in themselves only. For, this being no charity, but rather a co-partnership, there is no need of having any governor, treasurer, director, or other commanding officer but what may be chosen among themselves; and as the money is their own, they are the fittest persons to keep it.

2. That, after they have obtained his Majesty's sanction and are become a body corporate, under what name or title they shall think fit, they may choose from among themselves one treasurer, two wardens, and such other officers they shall deem proper, which officers shall have annual rotation, and new ones be chosen every year.

3. That, instead of consuming all or a great part of the stock in building, which would nip the project in the bud, they shall rent a convenient hall or house in town or country at their own option, which house must be equally divided into apartments. And, to save another great expense, as well as to prevent partiality or disgust, 'tis fit that every person furnish their own apartment, which furniture they may bequeath to whom they please. For, as all the members of the college are to be upon an equal footing, 'tis highly necessary there should not be the least distinction among them in diet, lodging, &c. And if one person dresses or furnishes better than another, there will be no need of complaint, because they do it at their own charge; though, to speak my mind, it would look most lovely to have a decent equality and uniformity in dress.

4. The kitchen, the infirmary, and other offices to be furnished at the common expense, but not to be taken out of the joint stock; on the contrary, every person to pay an equal proportion, which cannot amount to above two guineas a head. But in case the joint stock increases, the money to be refunded.

5. That they call a court among themselves as often as they shall think fit, at which every member shall have an equal vote, the treasurer taking the chair. At these courts everything shall be settled, all bargains made, all accounts audited, servants hired or displaced, the diet and college hours settled, and bye-laws made or amended as occasion or the general consent shall point out.

6. As all are to share the benefit, it may readily be supposed that the best advantage will be made of the money; but, above all, that they will go on a sure footing, and content themselves with the less interest upon the greater security. Though I must confess I know of no safer and more profitable method than to lend money on proper deposits, as goods, merchandises, &c., after the manner of the charitable corporation in Fenchurch Street. This, or some such sure method, may bring in twenty per cent. on their money, which will considerably increase their capital, better their provisions, &c., and in time make them a very wealthy body. But in case no more than five per cent. interest be produced from their capital of twenty thousand pounds, it will amount to one thousand pounds per annum; which may be laid out after this or the like manner:—

|  | Per Annum. |
|---|---|
| To a Physician . . . . . | £20  0  0 |
| To a Clerk for the Treasury . . . | 20  0  0 |
| To a Chaplain . . . . . | 20  0  0 |
| To a Cook . . . . . | 10  0  0 |
| To a Laundry-maid . . . . | 5  0  0 |
| To a Housemaid . . . . | 5  0  0 |
| To two Nurses for the Infirmary . . | 20  0  0 |
|  | £100  0  0 |

These salaries may be enlarged as the college increases in wealth, or the whole subscription may be doubled at first, and everything in proportion. But as this is only a sketch or rough draft, further particulars from me would be needless. Besides, I am but a poor calculator, and only give the hint to the public as my duty to my fellow-Christians. I wish for nothing more than to see it improved, and if I don't properly explain myself, people must be so charitable to think for me; for I write even this under many bodily infirmities, and am so impatient to have done that I forget half I have to say. But to proceed:—

The salaries amounting to a hundred pounds a year, and allowing another hundred for a house, till there shall be overplus enough to build one, there remains just eight hundred pounds per annum for provision.

If this should be deficient, it will easily be made up out of the overplus which will accrue.

1st, From making better advantage of their money than is here proposed.

2ndly, From the money paid at the admission of new members, as the old ones die. And,

3rdly, From the legacies which the old members may leave to augment the stock; for, if but one member die in a year, there is four hundred pounds to be added to the thousand, which will considerably augment every article. If more should die, or legacies be left, the stock will increase, and consequently the interest thereof will make allowance for greater expenses, and by degrees render the whole more noble and magnificent.

Excuse, gentle reader, my immethodical manner of calculating, and help me out the best you can, for I have forgot some things which ought to have been mentioned before; but, writing just as they occur, I must leave the whole to be methodised and amended by a clearer head and a more able hand.

I have mentioned salaries without prescribing for what. Give me leave therefore to assign the officers their proper employments.

The Treasurer must have care of the cash, and the Chairman of all committees.

The Wardens must look after the provisions, agree with all tradesmen, and superintend the accounts.

The Physician must visit twice a week, or oftener if need be, and prescribe to the sick members ; he may likewise appoint the apothecary, inspect his medicines, and tax his bills.

The Clerk or Bookkeeper must be constantly in the accompting-house, to set down every particular, to minute the proceeding of committees, to keep the account of cash, and, in a word, to take the trouble of writing off the Treasurer and Warden's hands ; he must diet in the house. As also,

The Chaplain, some sober, elderly, decayed clergyman of good morals, to read prayers morning and evening, and every Sunday a sermon out of Bishop Tillotson, Dr Scott, Dr South, or some other sound divine. And, to further this good work, I myself will present the college with a handsome Bible and Common Prayer Book, and all the sermons above mentioned, if I live to see it finished ; and if I die before, I have made proper provision in my will.

The Cook must dress the victuals, keep clean the kitchen, pantry, and cellar.

The Laundry-maid must wash and mend their linen and wait at table.

The Housemaid must make the beds, sweep the rooms, and wait at table.

The two Nurses must attend the infirmary, and sit up alternately if need be ; and when none are sick, they must help, get up and mend the linen, and assist the other servants, as the Treasurer and Wardens shall appoint.

As the thing increases, so may the servants and their wages. A Porter, a Butler, a Scullion, and other servants may be added as the members think fit.

To crown all, let the whole be independent and among themselves; let them always keep the staff in their own hands, and never subject themselves to treasurers, &c., out of their own body. Let them accept of no charities, but do as many as they are able; and, in a word, let them keep up the grandeur of the design to such a pitch that their friends and relations may not be ashamed to visit them, but, on the contrary, be proud they are of such a body. Let the election of new members be vested only in themselves, and let them choose only such as shall give reputation to the college.

In a word, I have drawn up my scheme in general terms, it being intended for the benefit of either sex. 'Tis indifferent whether the ladies compose a college, and call themselves sisters, or any other name they shall think fit; or whether a college be composed of gentlemen, under the title of brothers, fellows, or any other denomination; our Protestant Monastery is still the same; nor can a name alter its property, or make it less beneficial or commendable.

THE END

Printed by BALLANTYNE, HANSON & CO.
Edinburgh & London